MW00773505

THE BUDDHA WHO DROVE A BENTLEY

LIVE YOUR MOST AUTHENTIC LIFE, FIND TRUE HAPPINESS, AND HAVE IT ALL

THE BUDDHA WHO DROVE A BENTLEY

LIVE YOUR MOST AUTHENTIC LIFE, FIND TRUE HAPPINESS, AND HAVE IT ALL

ALESSANDRO TRONCO

ethos
collective

THE BUDDHA WHO DROVE A BENTLEY
© 2023 by Alessandro Tronco. All rights reserved.

Printed in the United States of America

Published by Ethos Collective™
PO Box 43, Powell, OH 43065
www.ethoscollective.vip

LCCN: 2023905879
Paperback ISBN: 978-1-63680-155-1
Hardcover ISBN: 978-1-63680-156-8
e-book ISBN: 978-1-63680-157-5

Available in paperback, hardcover, e-book, and audiobook

Cover design by Michael Ostuno

Dedication

To my beloved daughters, Julia, Isabella, and Olivia, and my cherished wife, Gina, this book is dedicated with profound love and gratitude. Your steadfast support has been the cornerstone of my writing journey, and I am immensely thankful for the courage you have instilled in me to embark on this transformative endeavor.

This book is a testament to the strength of our family and the transformative power of love. It is a reflection of the remarkable bond we share and the profound impact we have had on one another. Through the highs and lows of this creative journey, you have stood by me, offering solace, encouragement, and a safe haven in which to pour my heart and soul.

May this story touch the lives of others, both positively and negatively, as it has affected ours. May it serve as a beacon of hope, resilience, and unwavering faith that propels us forward. As we continue to navigate life's unpredictable path, I am forever grateful to have each of you by my side. Together, we are unstoppable, and with God's grace, our collective story will unfold in magnificent ways.

With all my love and gratitude,

Alessandro Tronco

Table of Contents

Foreword

People have a distorted view of the American Dream. By societal standards, I had everything that encompasses that fabled dream: money, cars and planes, and a successful career as a businessman. And like Alessandro Tronco, all the material possessions couldn't fill the void inside me and the despair I felt.

Decisions and missteps we make along our journey don't have to determine our destination. We have resources and new choices to make at every step. That is why I find *The Buddha Who Drove a Bentley* to be such a powerful book. I love the story of an overcomer. When someone digs deep, exhibits the courage to face and heal their past, and exercises personal or professional leadership, it ignites my soul.

I consider Alessandro to be an expert on transforming lives. Forget theory. He's lived it, and thankfully, he's converted this wisdom into a beautiful fable. Get ready to grow even more and overcome challenges you never thought possible.

—Gerard Armond Powell, author of *Sh*t the Moon Said: A Story of Sex, Drugs and Ayahuasca*, and founder of Rythmia Life Advancement Center, the #1 rated Specialty Lodging in the world

Chapter One

What good is it for a man to gain the whole world,
and yet lose or forfeit his very self?

—Luke 9:25

The sun hadn't risen yet as ten-year-old Vincent maneuvered in the dark around the small apartment he lived in with his parents, older brother, and two older sisters in Sicily. It was his duty as one of the sons in the family to contribute to the household that struggled daily to make ends meet. He felt his way along the wall that had chips of paint missing—it hadn't been painted since the apartment was new decades prior—until he reached the antiquated light switch for the kitchen. The light flickered several times before settling into its dim, steady glow. It would probably need replacing soon, but most things in his home did.

His mother's efforts to make their modest apartment a nurturing home didn't go unnoticed by Vincent. No matter their financial struggles, she worked hard to provide her children with a safe and loving environment and did her best to give them everything they needed. His mother set an example of strength and courage that Vincent would try to live up to in the years to come.

Although Vincent's father worked hard to provide for his family, the lingering pain of the hardships and sadness from his upbringing stayed with him and often manifested in excessive drinking and outbursts of anger. The internal walls his father built up made it difficult for Vincent to connect with him. Despite all this, he loved his father deeply and never stopped trying to bridge the gap between them. He hoped he could make things right one day and heal their broken bond.

Vincent's older brother, Massimo, was rarely around. It seemed like he intentionally kept his distance from the family. However, Massimo was always available to listen when Vincent needed someone to talk to and let him hang out with him and his friends, which made Vincent feel special. And he always stepped in to defend and protect Vincent when he got picked on by kids at school.

Vincent wondered if his brother was burdened with secrets. While this made it difficult for him to connect with Massimo, there was love between the two brothers.

Amid the chaos of working and going to school, Vincent found his only source of joy in his two sisters, Marilena and Cristina. Despite his difficult circumstances, their beauty, intelligence, and vibrant personalities filled their home with life. He cherished every moment spent laughing and conversing with them, for it temporarily distracted him from his struggles. He found comfort in their company, and whenever his worries weighed him down, their laughter lifted him up.

Together they would stay up late, dreaming of what life could be like if things were different. Although they had to remain in the apartment more often than not, Vincent was grateful for his time with them. Their love was strong and brought light to a time of darkness—darkness that went deeper than anyone knew.

When Marilena and Cristina weren't around, Vincent found solace in daydreaming about how he could one day live a better life. He was determined to escape the confines of poverty and become rich and famous. And this was another reason he was leaving the house hours before school would start.

Although his family needed the extra money, Vincent could have easily done jobs other children his age would do. Instead, he headed out into the streets of his hometown with a battered suitcase in one hand—filled with homemade delicacies, herbs, cheese, olives, cured meats, fish, and bread—and his father's pocket watch gripped tightly in the other. Too many times, Vincent had gotten into trouble for being late to school, which resulted in his father feeling even more disappointed in his son. While the watch was a reminder to get to school on time, it also felt connected to an invisible chain around Vincent's neck, weighing him down with his father's expectations to make something of himself.

The young entrepreneur sold the items door-to-door throughout the city, traveling whatever distance necessary to make sales happen. Every day brought new challenges and new opportunities to learn. Vincent taught himself to barter effectively against experienced traders and deal with customers who did not value honesty or quality. He grew to understand how to maximize profits while still providing a fair price. These streets also taught him how to navigate crowded marketplaces without getting lost and avoid dangerous areas.

What started as merely a way for Vincent to pay for food for his family eventually turned into something bigger—a business venture that could potentially provide greater stability and security for them in years to come. Still, this was no easy feat for such a young boy. Many people underestimated or thought ill of him because of his age, but he slowly won them over through hard work and dedication. Even those who initially refused to buy from him changed their tune after they saw what he could do.

The older vendors started to look upon the young boy with admiration. They couldn't believe how much determination this little kid had. He worked harder than most adults twice his age and never complained about anything despite having so few hours in the day; nothing stopped him from pursuing what he wanted most out of life.

☥

As Vincent grew older, his desire to achieve more pushed him to follow one of his favorite daydreams: going to America. At sixteen, he booked passage to New York, leaving behind his family, friends, and possessions. It was a difficult decision to make, but he knew there were greater opportunities in America, and he wanted to take advantage of them. As much as he feared the unknown and dreaded leaving everything familiar behind him, Vincent found hope in the thought that one day he would be able to provide a better life for himself and his loved ones, which moved him forward with optimism in his heart.

As soon as Vincent set foot on Ellis Island, he looked around in awe and confusion. He had no money or friends, and he didn't know any English. How would he survive, let alone thrive? His heart raced because this was his chance for a better life, and he refused to let fear or doubt stop him from achieving greatness, even though the odds seemed to be stacked against him.

With a deep breath, he took a step, pushing forward as if driven by an unseen force. He may have faced many struggles throughout his journey from Italy to America, but these experiences only made him stronger. Despite the language barrier and cultural differences, he proceeded with courage in his heart.

Vincent's optimism shifted to despair, fear, and loneliness as he trudged through each day, struggling to make ends meet with no friends or family around to support him. No matter how hard he worked, his mountain seemed insurmountable to climb. Unwilling to give up, his strength and resilience never wavered—he took each day as it came and prayed that his troubles eventually would be alleviated. He was a fighter, after all, and had been for as long as he could remember.

Often, Vincent recalled the hard work he put in at home as a salesman. This memory helped him press on, one step at a time, never giving up despite all odds. He knew better days were ahead if he could just stay the course. With his head high and faith in his heart, he continued to fight for a better life—one filled with hope and joy. He seized every opportunity presented to him so that he could finally turn his dreams into reality.

Vincent continued to search for jobs, no matter how arduous or thankless they may have been. And there were times when he felt embarrassed for what he had to do to survive, like when he had to stand in line to collect food stamps. No matter how many times he had to move from one bad apartment to the other, and regardless of how much poverty and desperation crushed his soul, he kept fighting. He was proud of himself for doing whatever it took to survive.

Slowly, the clouds cleared, and Vincent felt his suffering subside. Bit by bit, he watched his hardships melt away, replaced with happiness, contentment, and peace. With courage and perseverance, he made it through the darkest days and knew better days were ahead. He had found the courage to continue through the storm and emerged a stronger, wiser person.

The word of God was an anchor for Vincent. He believed that God loves each one of us unconditionally, only desires what's best for us, and would provide the abundance and prosperity Vincent sought once he surrendered his worries and fears to him. God promises that he will never abandon or leave us without hope for a better future, and Vincent knew he could trust that promise. He repeated these words in his mind when things felt hopeless.

The experience gained from selling on the streets at ten taught Vincent nothing was impossible. Despite his humble beginnings, he believed he could still make something of himself, and he worked hard to build a better future for himself and those around him.

Vincent never gave up on himself or his dreams—no matter how difficult the journey became, he kept pushing forward. Years after arriving in America, this foundation of perseverance would set him up as an example for other immigrants—a reminder that even if it seems impossible, anything is possible if you just keep fighting.

Throughout the journey, he never forgot the importance of family. Though they were far away, their love and support carried him through each difficult moment. He also found strength in his friends—those who listened to his stories, shared their own experiences, and inspired him with their courage and determination. These relationships kept him going when hope seemed lost. Together, they helped him find a place of belonging in America—a place he could finally call home.

His struggles may have been challenging and trying, but ultimately, his courage allowed him to find great wealth and fame in America. One day, after starting his own family, Vincent decided to take a chance on an idea that had been brewing in his mind for some time. Although his savings were meager, he invested everything he had into the project, knowing that it could make or break him; it would be either a tremendous success or an abject failure.

Fortunately for Vincent and his family, it was the former—his project flourished, and within a few years, he had become one of the wealthiest men in the country. Money flowed to him without effort; every endeavor he undertook succeeded as if by magic. He rose rapidly through the ranks of the business elite, and people everywhere sought him out for advice and guidance.

With each passing year, Vincent's wealth grew exponentially, even expanding overseas into other countries. He was considered one of the most influential businessmen in all of America and beyond—not bad for someone who once could barely afford food or clothing.

Vincent had it all: power and money. But despite his impressive achievements, he couldn't shake the empty feeling that had been with him since he was a child. His relationships with his family and closest friends were strong, yet the void remained unfulfilled, and nothing satisfied it. Expensive cars, designer clothes, luxury vacations—nothing could sate his hunger for something deeper. No matter how much money or success he amassed, the emptiness still lingered like an unwelcome guest in his life.

At night, Vincent would lie awake in bed wondering why he felt adrift in the world despite having everything that *should* make him happy: a loving family, wonderful kids, and even a beautiful wife who supported him through thick and thin. He questioned why none of these things could fill the hollowness surrounding his heart like an invisible barrier between himself and true happiness. As he pondered this conundrum day after day, year after year, he began to realize that maybe contentment does not come from what surrounds us but rather from within us.

One night after watching the hours tick by, Vincent quietly rose from his bed and took his expensive sports car for a drive, though he had no destination in mind. Maybe some answer would come to him. He could feel the weight of the world pushing against his chest, a tightness like no other. The thought of getting lost appealed to him, so he decided that was what he would do.

Vincent drove for hours on end, passing through towns and cities until, eventually, he found himself in the middle of the mountains. The roads were winding and narrow; he had only trees, animals, and darkness for company. The air was thick with anticipation and something else: something undefinable, a feeling Vincent hadn't experienced before.

As Vincent drove further into the mountains, his windows fogged up, and the only sound he could hear was the quiet hum of his tires on the pavement. It felt as if he had stepped into another world, one where his troubles no longer seemed so big or important but still lingered like an ever-present reminder of his insignificance amidst an indifferent universe that simply carried on regardless.

Tiny snowflakes sprinkled against his windshield. All of Vincent's pondering seemed pointless; his heart wasn't truly in it anymore. Instead, he just wanted to be somewhere far away where nobody knew who he was or what he was doing, somewhere peaceful with no obligations or expectations beyond what was natural and right for him.

Eventually, after shifting through countless blind turns, Vincent found himself at the top of a hill overlooking a valley below. Snow-covered hillsides stretching out as far as the eye could see framed frozen water underneath a night sky filled with stars twinkling down upon them all. There was beauty in the harsh landscape, and he felt momentarily tranquil.

Suddenly, he sensed something wasn't right. Out of the corner of his eye, he saw a car approaching from behind with its headlights blazing. Instinctively, he swerved . . .

Chapter Two

Rejoice always.

—1 Thessalonians 5:16

eautiful music, people laughing—these were the sounds that Vincent was first aware of. Next, the scents of fresh foods from all over the world filled the air, prompting him to open his eyes. It took a few blinks to adjust to the bright lights surrounding him. *Wasn't it just nighttime?* As he surveyed his surroundings, he realized he was standing in a beautiful place full of color and life. Everyone looked happy and carefree.

The disoriented feelings he awoke with eased as he walked around this new mystical place. Feelings of loneliness and emptiness that weighed him down for years dissolved as he observed the other people's interactions. And those people didn't look at him with judging eyes because he was a stranger. Instead, they smiled and waved as he passed or offered him some food.

Although he wasn't ready to fully embrace his new surroundings yet, Vincent could feel he would join his new friends, smiling and laughing soon. It seemed to him that everyone could express themselves without fear; they were in a place of belonging. As his feet led him through seemingly endless streets, he felt a deep desire to experience life like they were. Everyone seemed content in the moment and radiated such joyful energy. *When was the last time I felt so free of burden?*

Vincent's spirit sensed the connections surrounding him. Everyone seemed connected to each other, Mother Nature, and a deeper meaning of life. He didn't know how he knew this, but he also had no desire to question this knowledge. There was joy in just knowing, and a spark of hope ignited in Vincent that he might be able to tap into that knowledge too. A connection with Mother Earth had been part of him since he was a child, but life and his desire to succeed had suppressed it.

As if created by his thoughts, Vincent noticed a tree growing in the center of a cobblestone street ahead of him. He approached it with curiosity, reaching out his hand to touch the tree's trunk to confirm it was real. The tree seemed to welcome his touch, and Vincent felt warmth and acceptance spread throughout him. It felt as if God had brought him to this place to learn something.

"How have I gotten so caught up in my day-to-day obligations that I've forgotten everything else that's important in life?" Vincent asked the tree.

Although the tree didn't reply, the sensation of being accepted as he was at that moment continued to emanate throughout Vincent's body. Still, he had questions. How would he ever make sense of it all and reconnect to what truly mattered in life? Despite the questions and complications that raced through his mind, Vincent didn't feel frustrated.

As he continued his walk, he transitioned from the town into a jungle. Wandering through the trees, Vincent breathed in the lush, tropical scents. The sun had shifted since he first arrived, casting a beautiful golden light through the jungle. He felt at peace. The serenity of this place was unmatched by any other Vincent's travels had taken him over the years.

It felt like Vincent had stepped into an entirely different world. Birds sang their evening songs, a soft trickle of water nearby echoed around him, and even a few brightly-colored butterflies fluttered past him. With each step, he felt more connected with nature and his inner self, as if he had reawakened a part of himself long since buried. A sense of clarity settled over him, and he somehow knew that no matter where life took him, he would remember this moment in the jungle forever.

As the stars appeared above him to light his way, Vincent came across a casita in a clearing. He approached cautiously, but when he opened the door, he felt that it was made specifically for him. Taking a moment to appreciate the day's journey, he realized he wanted to keep his newfound sense of tranquility and clarity close to his heart always. Exhaustion washed over him, and Vincent collapsed onto the bed and fell asleep faster than he'd done since childhood.

Chapter Three

*The Lord detests lying lips, but he delights
in people who are trustworthy.*

—Proverbs 12:22

The morning brought a renewed sense of serenity. After eating a plate of fruit waiting for him on the small table inside the casita, Vincent decided to explore more of the magical land he was in. He wandered through the jungle for most of the day, appreciating the smallest details. His soul was coming to life again through enjoying the simple beauty of Mother Nature.

As the sun began setting, Vincent started to return to the casita when he came across a beautiful young woman who radiated with life.

"Hello, Vincent. I'm Julia," she said and then smiled. Her words and presence were calming yet powerful. Even the stars in the sky seemed brighter because of her smile.

Vincent started to speak but then was at a loss for words. Julia's beauty was so pure—it radiated from within, and it defied description.

Julia's smile persisted. "Come, sit with me.".

Mesmerized by the young woman's energy and drawn to the light that emanated from her, Vincent nodded and followed her to sit under a tree.

The two told stories about their lives, laughed with each other, and Vincent even shared some of his darker secrets with Julia. It seemed natural; he felt more open-minded and enlightened in her presence.

Julia wasn't an ordinary woman, he could tell. Through their conversations, she had opened his heart in ways he thought impossible. Looking at her, Vincent was reminded of the power of love and beauty within us all.

"Look up at the stars," Julia said after allowing Vincent time to reflect quietly.

Vincent hadn't *really* looked at the night sky at any point in his life. Sure, he'd seen stars and noticed when more stars were visible when he traveled outside cities. But he never took the time to really look at them. *Why have I never looked up at these before? Do these stars exist back home?* As he allowed the internal dialogue to cease and gazed upward, he was mesmerized by the immediate connection he felt. He felt his spirit merging with the stars. Each one was a reminder of infinite possibilities. Vincent wanted to carry this feeling with him always.

The stars glittered above them like softly glowing diamonds—a heavenly canopy protecting their treasured moment together.

"In order to fulfill pure joy, happiness, and a connection with God and Earth," Julia began, although her voice wasn't startling to Vincent, "you must always tell the truth at all costs. You will discover your path forward by understanding the importance of truth and living in alignment."

Vincent knew he'd been hiding in fear and shame because of truths he kept concealed. Still, he didn't feel judged by Julia's words and realized he must take them to heart.

Julia continued speaking her wisdom. "Truth is an integral part of life and something we should strive to seek out in all things. It's important to be mindful that truth doesn't come easy and often requires effort to discover." She paused to allow her words to enter Vincent's mind, then said, "Once you find truth, the rewards are immense: peace of mind, clarity of thought, and a deeper understanding of life's complexities, bringing us closer to our highest selves."

Vincent continued to gaze at the stars, internalizing Julia's wise words. *I want to know my highest self,* he thought. *I want to lead a more meaningful life.*

As if Julia could hear his thoughts, she said, "Instead of merely chasing after fleeting desires or relying on external factors for validation, truth allows us to gain the courage needed to make conscious choices that reflect our values and purpose, leading to a more meaningful life."

The stars had shifted in the sky, and Vincent could tell it was getting late even though he didn't feel tired. As the comfortable silence lingered between the two, Julia pulled out a cross and handed it to Vincent.

Vincent ran his fingers over the gift, studying it in the starlight. The cross was made from bamboo, as best he could tell. It was bendable and lightweight but tremendously strong.

"It is a reminder that truth is what God wants us to seek. It's the path toward inner peace, contentment, and connection with everyone around us. May truth continue to light the path ahead of you, Vincent." Julia stood, preparing to leave, and added, "Truth is the way."

Julia disappeared into the night, though Vincent remained seated under the tree, holding onto the cross. The lesson he learned from her was invaluable and had shifted something inside him. After taking a deep breath, he rose and repeated, "Truth is the way," before returning to the casita, feeling full of love and a newfound respect for truth and its potential to bring him closer to his true self.

Chapter Four

*Not only so, but we also glory in our sufferings,
because we know that suffering produces perseverance.*

—Romans 5:3

The following morning, Vincent awoke but remained in bed with his eyes closed. He consciously internalized the appreciation of his newfound understanding of how truth could transform his life. As he pushed himself out of bed and stretched, he felt twenty years younger and ready to take on anything.

After enjoying the healthy breakfast awaiting him, Vincent walked outside the casita into the morning sun, its soft, warm light seeming to welcome everything it touched. Appreciating his surroundings reminded him of the lesson Julia had taught him the night before: Living with truth as a guide will lead to a path of greater peace, contentment, and connection with people. Vincent smiled, knowing this new day was full of possibilities and potential.

Vincent spent the morning walking through the foreign jungle, appreciating the beauty of his surroundings and the peace he felt in his soul. As the sun shifted above him, the lush scents accompanying him on his walk changed into the aroma of food. He pressed his palm against his grumbling stomach and followed the smell that lured him back to the town he was in the day before. His feet carried him down a cobblestone street and into an alley where a small restaurant was tucked away. No sign indicated the establishment's name, yet he knew with certainty this was the source of food beckoning him.

As Vincent pushed the door open, the richness of the aromas of the food cooking almost brought tears to his eyes. The red brick walls encapsulated an establishment from another decade, filled with love and home-cooked meals. He continued taking in the welcoming atmosphere as he sat at the antique wood table closest to the kitchen.

Vincent sipped water and appreciated the soft music playing in the background that added to the ambiance. After setting his empty glass on the table, he noticed a beautiful young woman walking toward him. Her thick, dark brown curls cascading down her back bounced as she gracefully approached him, exuding a palpable air of confidence. Following her closely, a beautiful German Shepherd with a smooth black and brown coat trotted loyally beside her. Occasionally, the dog would look up at the woman with its compassionate eyes.

"Hello. I'm Isabella," the woman said as she stopped at Vincent's table.

Isabella set a plate of food on the table in front of Vincent, but he barely registered her gesture. Instead, he studied the woman and instinctively knew her beauty and charm went deeper than her outward appearance. She had an aura about her that shone brighter than any light source could ever hope to attain. Her movements and words embodied kindness, compassion, and a warmth that resonated from her heart.

"Please eat," Isabella instructed kindly, then left with her dog for Vincent to enjoy his meal.

The aroma and presentation of the meal were exquisite, but it paled in comparison to the flavor of the food. Vincent could taste the care and love that went into making the meal. Savoring each bite, he felt as if he were in a culinary paradise. It was a unique experience that left him feeling content and at peace.

As Vincent reached for his wallet to pay for the cuisine, a sudden panic washed over him. *Where is my wallet? Why would I come into a restaurant without being able to pay?* He felt a soft hand rest against his forearm, instantly distracting him from his frantic search.

"I have something very important to talk to you about," Isabella began. "Suffering."

Vincent swallowed hard, wondering whether this was the speech given to people who didn't pay for their meal.

Isabella smiled warmly. "I want to talk to you about your suffering," she said. "Are you familiar with Samudaya? Buddhists believe this is the root of all spiritual affliction and dissatisfaction. Samudaya is Sanskrit and means 'coming together.'"

Isabella paused to let Vincent process what she was saying, then continued. "It refers to all causes, conditions, and tendencies that lead us to experience suffering. There are three main components of Samudaya: clinging or attachment, ignorance, and craving or desire. Each one of these aspects has an important role to play when it comes to experiencing suffering."

"How does this relate to my suffering?" Vincent asked, his brows coming together.

Isabella spoke to Vincent without judgment. "When we cling or attach ourselves to something, we hope it'll provide us security. But it ultimately leads to suffering. Grasping at something too strongly because it makes us feel secure or comfortable at that moment makes us blind to recognizing its impermanence."

Vincent leaned forward in his chair, nodding.

"Ignorance is the general lack of knowledge and understanding about ourselves, others, and life. In the long run, lacking knowledge about life's truths and how certain things may impact us emotionally or spiritually causes us to remain ignorant of what can help or hurt us instead of learning from life's lessons."

There was truth in Isabella's explanation that resonated with Vincent. He felt how deeply his suffering ran inside him but pushed it down to remain focused on everything she said.

"And finally," Isabella said, "we crave or desire things outside ourselves to make us feel happy or fulfilled. However, when we crave something too much, like material goods or success, we create an obsession. No matter how much we obtain, there will always be more, and our needs will never be truly satisfied."

Vincent didn't know how to respond to Isabella. He felt everything she said applied to him and how he'd been living his life. "How do I change this?"

"Placing too much emphasis on materialism can lead to unhappiness or dissatisfaction because the focus is constantly on acquiring more instead of simply enjoying what you already have. You focus too much on material things and the pursuit of success," Isabella said matter-of-factly but not accusingly.

"I always feel stressed and anxious," Vincent admitted. "There always seems to be more to accomplish so I can provide everything my family wants."

"Placing too much emphasis on materialism leads to unhappiness and dissatisfaction because the focus is on constantly acquiring more. Have you ever taken time to appreciate what you have?" Isabella asked. Without waiting for his answer, she continued. "Success isn't always measured by what we acquire or accomplish. Instead, it can come from within as one learns to appreciate themselves for who they are rather than how much they can buy or achieve."

Sadness enveloped Vincent as he processed Isabella's wisdom. He knew he'd been caught up in chasing money and material things and suddenly felt like none of it mattered. All his efforts to acquire the wealth he'd dreamed of in his childhood had not filled the emptiness inside him. It did the opposite, in fact, and he felt the vastness of the hollowness within. "Something is missing from my life," he said, although he intended that to be a thought rather than something he shared with the young sage at his table.

"Perhaps you're looking for fulfillment in the wrong places," Isabella said kindly. "True joy and contentment can't be bought; it has to come from within."

Vincent frowned and looked down at the table. He remembered that every time he purchased something new and extravagant, it only brought an immediate sense of joy. As soon as the moment had passed, he inevitably found himself back in the depths of despair. He was stuck in a never-ending cycle of purchasing items, hoping they would bring him some fulfillment, only to be disappointed when they did not live up to his expectations. Hopelessness weighed heavily on Vincent's mind and soul; no matter how hard he tried, it never seemed enough. "I've wasted so much energy chasing after fleeting things that could never bring real satisfaction or meaning," he said as he raised his eyes to look up at Isabella again.

He saw kindness and understanding in Isabella's expression. "There's a way to end your suffering," she said. "Magga is another fundamental teaching of Buddhism. It means 'the middle way' and is the path to wisdom. There are steps you must take, though. The first is recognizing the reality of suffering and dissatisfaction in your life. In order to do this, you must turn inward and observe your reactions to feelings and sensations. This will allow you to uncover the root cause of your suffering."

It seemed appropriate for Vincent to close his eyes and attempt to uncover the source of his suffering. At first, his mind strayed in many directions. Slowly, he narrowed his thoughts down to what was important to the conversation. As if someone was speaking through him, he said, "Attachment."

Isabella replied to Vincent, whose eyes were still closed. "Attachment can manifest in various forms. For you, Vincent, it has been an attachment for accumulating material possessions and success."

Vincent opened his eyes and nodded at her. Even the acknowledgment of this being the source brought him a sense of hope.

"The next step is to cultivate mindfulness to understand yourself better and gain insight into the nature of reality. Mindfulness helps us become aware of our thoughts and emotions without getting swept away by them. Furthermore, it allows us to identify patterns in our behavior so we can ultimately make changes that lead us toward liberation from suffering. So, it's important to be consciously aware of your thoughts and emotions."

Isabella explained this in a way that felt like an important assignment to Vincent. "I will take more time to be mindful."

A comforting smile appeared on Isabella's face. "Good. Now, the third step involves cultivating wisdom or insight (paññā). To do this, you must reflect deeply upon what we have learned through mindfulness practices so far, seeing clearly how your attachments are causing suffering and learning how to let them go. The goal is not just understanding ideas but penetrating deeply into truths, such as impermanence and dependent origination, so these realizations become deeply ingrained within our being."

Vincent felt like he should've been taking notes on everything Isabella was saying. But there was a sensation telling him that everything she said was being absorbed into his subconscious, stored for him to access as he moved forward in his healing.

"Finally, the fourth step is developing ethical principles based on these insights into the true nature of life's experiences. The aim is to practice what you've learned by engaging in generous acts with an open heart, remaining mindful in all situations we encounter, speaking kindly to others, and treating ourselves with kindness and compassion. Doing this will allow you to remain free from attachment-based suffering even amidst challenge and adversity."

With those final words of wisdom, Isabella rose from her seat. "You mustn't be afraid of your suffering. This, too, shall pass." She leaned forward and kissed Vincent tenderly on the forehead before returning to the kitchen with her dog to prepare a meal for the next visitor.

Vincent left the restaurant with hope and a lot to contemplate. As he walked the path back to his casita, he thought about how he would focus on appreciating everything he had going forward.

Chapter Five

*…as far as the east is from the west, so far has he removed
our transgressions from us.*

—Psalm 103:12

After hours of walking through the thick, humid jungle, Vincent stopped to look around and ponder the conversation with Isabella the day prior. *This, too, shall pass.* Her words resonated deeply with him in the warm afternoon. He hadn't seen another living soul since he began his journey that morning. But he kept scanning the distance, hoping to see something else ahead of him. Suddenly, a small structure far ahead came into focus as if appearing magically.

Though exhausted, a spark of hope ignited in Vincent, and he moved at a quicker pace toward the building. As he neared it, the structure he mistook for a small hut transformed into a church, radiant in sunlight that shone down purposefully on it. His heart fluttered as he walked the path toward the door and entered.

A light breeze blew through the interior when Vincent crossed the threshold, filling him with an eerie calmness. The interior was plain but elegant in its simplicity. Only a few pews lined each side, with an aisle down the middle leading to a wooden cross with candles burning on both sides.

Like so many other times while he'd been in this surreal land, Vincent's feet carried him toward the cross without consciously thinking about it. He admired the symbol as he knelt and crossed himself—a reflex after years of attending Mass as a child in Italy. With a bowed head and closed eyes, he whispered, "God, please give me guidance in this unfamiliar land."

Before Vincent could continue his prayer, a voice in his mind caused him to pause. *Do not fear. No matter how uncertain you feel or how far you travel from home and comfort, you can walk with courage and hope. Beauty can be found even in the darkest places if you look hard enough.*

Vincent's eyes shot open. He immediately blinked, trying to adjust his eyes to the single-lit candle in the darkness surrounding him. He wasn't sure if he was still in the same bright, welcoming church but didn't have time to answer that question before a figure approached him.

Light brighter than the candle emanated from the beautiful woman with long, curly hair cascading over her shoulders who moved as gracefully as a swan on still waters. Her hazel eyes twinkled like stars as they gazed kindly at Vincent. But the smile on her perfect cupid's bow lips made her stand out, radiating peace and serenity throughout his soul.

Vincent was positive his heartbeat could be heard throughout the room. *Am I dreaming?* He thought he noticed the woman shake her head like she could hear his thoughts. At that moment, it seemed like something shifted inside him—an awakening—and he knew the woman was the cause.

"Hello, Vincent," the woman said, her voice as angelic as the rest of her.

"Hi," Vincent said, trying to mask the shakiness in his voice. He was in awe of the stranger but also knew she was important, special.

"Don't be afraid," she said with a soft laugh. "My name is Gina, and I'm here specifically to bring love and forgiveness into your life."

Vincent swallowed hard. "You have?"

Gina's expression turned somber. "You've been so angry and hurt for such a long time," she said softly. "Isn't it time to let go of all that pain? To forgive the person who wronged you? For you to forgive yourself for all the hurt you've caused people and move forward without this weight on your shoulders?"

Vincent shook his head. He had lived with bitterness for so many years that he couldn't imagine life without it. "I broke my marriage vows when I betrayed my wife. I can't forgive myself for that." He felt the pain, shame, and guilt for everything he had done wrong in life were his punishment. The hurt and pain he had caused his wife and children when he had an affair constantly weighed heavily on him.

"Tell me about that," Gina said, kneeling beside Vincent.

After taking a deep breath to push down the lump in his throat, Vincent began. "It seems like yesterday when everything was perfect, and Marie and I were deeply in love. Our wedding day was exquisite: the sun shone brightly over the horizon, emphasizing every color in the sky. The

29

excitement of our guests was palpable. Everyone was anticipating this event as their favorite couple joined together as one. Marie looked breathtaking in her ivory gown as she walked toward me, surrounded by a sea of white rose petals." Vincent paused, feeling the excitement and hope he felt on that day. "Her veil danced over her face in the morning breeze, but I could see the love she carried with her."

The smile that had formed on Vincent's face started to fade. "We have three beautiful daughters, you know. They are the light of my life. But I made a mistake that hurt them and Marie. My indiscretions broke the trust between us. And no matter how hard Marie and I work to make things right again, things haven't felt the same. Lingering doubts on both sides replaced the harmony. We constantly question each other's intentions and words."

Gina remained silently listening.

Vincent couldn't close the floodgate Gina had opened with her simple request. "I remember the night Marie discovered my affair. The love and hope she had instantly shattered. Heartbroken, she sank to the floor in despair as tears streamed down her cheeks." He reached up and wiped away a tear that was running down the side of his face. "Then, she jumped up and ran into the bathroom, slamming the door closed. I stood outside, paralyzed by guilt and regret, asking if she was okay. Between heart-wrenching sobs, she desperately pleaded for me to leave her alone and never come back. But I couldn't walk away. I stayed by the bathroom door all night, listening until her sobs quieted and an even more unbearable silence took over."

Retelling those events to Gina made the pain return as sharply as he experienced it that fateful night. "My daughters stopped looking at me with admiration and love too. Every glance felt tainted by suspicion or disappointment.

My oldest daughter looked at me like she didn't know me anymore. My affair embarrassed my middle daughter. And then there was my youngest, who just silently wept as she tried to grasp the magnitude of my mistake and how it impacted her young life. These four beautiful women are my world. And because of my indiscretion, I've destroyed all our worlds."

"But you still carry the hope that someday they will forgive you, don't you?" Gina asked, placing her hand on Vincent's arm. "It can feel scary and overwhelming at first, but I promise you won't regret taking the step of forgiveness. Releasing this weight from your shoulders will give you a sense of freedom and peace unlike anything else. You'll be able to focus on the good things in life instead of living with so much anger and regret."

Vincent considered Gina's words carefully. He knew she was right, and deep down, he could feel the truth of what she said, but something still held him back from taking the leap of faith to forgive.

Gina smiled encouragingly. "You don't have to go through this alone, Vincent. I'll be here every step of the way, no matter where you are. All you have to do is close your eyes, and I will appear with all the support and under-standing you need. Remember, forgiveness is your only way out; forgiveness is your ticket to freedom."

Still unsure he could do it, Vincent nodded anyway, hoping his silent response would suffice for the moment.

"Are you familiar with this quote? 'Therefore, if anyone is in Christ, he is a new creation. The old has passed away; behold, the new has come'(2 Corinthians 5:17-18 English Standard Version)." Gina smiled at Vincent. "I want you to understand that the journey toward freedom begins with one small step: forgiveness. Forgiving yourself may be difficult, but ultimately, it'll be worth it. Forgiveness is the only way out. Everyone deserves it, including you. Don't be afraid to take that first step."

Gina added, "And make sure to offer the same forgiveness to those around you. Every wise person in history has said the same thing: to forgive one's wrongs is a sign of true courage. It's an act of bravely letting go of all the hurt caused by others or ourselves. Do this, and you'll have inner peace and understanding."

Vincent knew this was his chance to make the most of life and was determined not to miss it. The work would be challenging, but he was tired of carrying the burden of guilt with him. As he reflected on what Gina was saying, he realized that fear wouldn't be pushing him forward; love for himself and others and a love for a life filled with joy and freedom awaited him if he were brave enough to take that first step toward forgiveness.

"How do I start?" Vincent asked.

"For Buddha, the path toward forgiveness begins with self-reflection and contemplation. He taught his followers to look within themselves for any negative feelings toward others or themselves. This will help you understand why something happened so it doesn't happen again. Shamans view forgiveness as releasing trapped energy caused by anger or resentment. By forgiving another person, shamans believe it frees up our energy reserves so we can move on from the situation without carrying residual baggage into future experiences."

"Like the baggage I'm carrying," Vincent said.

Gina smiled at his response. "Yes. Jesus spoke of forgiveness too. He saw it as essential to living a good life filled with love for others. Matthew 6:12 says, 'Forgive us our debts, as we also have forgiven our debtors.'"

Vincent felt like he was finally internalizing what Gina was saying. "So, these words remind us to practice mercy and encourage us not to seek revenge when wronged by someone else. Instead, I should turn the other cheek rather than return hate for hate."

"Exactly," Gina said. "While each religious leader approaches the concept differently, their underlying message is the same: Learn how to let go, find peace within yourself through understanding, and use your power wisely." Gina rose and offered her hand to Vincent. "Now that you understand the power of forgiveness, come with me."

Gina led Vincent outside, where birds singing in the trees and wind blowing through their hair welcomed them. "How are you feeling?"

Vincent allowed the serene environment to embrace him, as he'd done with Gina's wisdom. "I feel the start of peace inside me, something I haven't felt in a very long time. Thank you for blessing me with understanding and insight today."

"Carry peace and forgiveness with you as you go forth," Gina said as she stepped back toward the church.

After nodding his head in appreciation toward Gina, Vincent returned to the path that had led him to the mystical building. He walked for a while in deep contemplation, and as the sun was setting, he came across a clearing hidden deep within the trees. In its center stood a small pool of water surrounded by lush greenery and wildflowers in full bloom. It was like something out of a dream—so peaceful and inviting that he couldn't help but pause before entering.

Vincent strolled casually around the pond's perimeter before settling down, resting back on the soft grasses. As he gazed at the canopy above, he felt an inexplicable sense of inner peace wash over him, as if all his worries were melting away with each passing moment spent in that magical place.

He stayed in that spot for hours, watching the light move across the sky until, eventually, night fell. Darkness blanketed everything save for stars twinkling far off in the distance above him like tiny beacons guiding home weary travelers who'd become lost along their journey—much like himself not so long ago. Everything around him seemed brighter—even in the dark—and more vibrant than ever before. Even the air felt different as it caressed his skin with its warm embrace.

"This world is beautiful," Vincent said to the stars. "If we take time to appreciate it, it's filled with endless possibilities."

This newfound appreciation filled Vincent's heart with overwhelming joy. It wasn't until he felt a cool streak on his cheek when the wind blew that he realized tears of happiness were streaming down his cheeks. Not only was he on the path of forgiveness, but he felt inspired to share the lessons he learned with others.

"Life is beautiful no matter how hard things seem sometimes," Vincent said to himself as he started his journey back to the casita for the night. Hope and determination fueled each step until he sank into a deep sleep in his bed.

Chapter Six

Forget the former things; do not dwell on the past.

—Isaiah 43:18

Birds chirping in the morning sun welcomed Vincent to a new day. A light wind blew through the trees as he stepped outside his temporary home, bringing the sweet fragrance of exotic flowers and beckoning him to travel a new path through the jungle.

While admiring the natural surroundings along the path, Vincent noticed something glittering around him. Taking a few steps off the trail, he squinted and saw golden statues reflecting the sunlight adorning Buddhist temple walls, accompanied by visions of angels. The sight was surreal. How had he not noticed all the temples before?

Every step Vincent took around the structures made him feel more peaceful. He knew that whatever spiritual enlightenment awaited him that day would be profound if he were open to receiving it.

In the distance, a temple caught Vincent's eye. It was taller than the others, and as he neared it, it was one of the most beautiful sights he'd ever seen. Its golden spires glinted in the sun, and its ornate decorations sparkled like stars in a night sky. Every inch seemed to be crafted with love and devotion, from intricate carvings to colorful mosaics. Vincent thought that all who had laid eyes upon it must have been filled with awe and reverence. It was truly a place where divine beings could reside.

Vincent opened the door without hesitation and immediately felt tranquility wash over him. As his eyes fluttered closed to absorb the influx of sensations, he breathed in the scent of incense. Soft music played in the background, and the presence of divine energy made the hair on his arms stand up in reverence.

After appreciating the atmosphere that welcomed all who sought reflection, contemplation, and personal transformation, Vincent stepped through the grand entrance and began exploring the temple grounds. He wandered through winding pathways lined with statues of various Buddhas and Bodhisattvas—figures representing compassion, patience, and wisdom who provided spiritual guidance for those seeking enlightenment on their journey toward inner peace—that led to a large courtyard garden. He imagined this was the ideal place for worshippers to gather to pray at dawn and dusk when the sunlight would filter through the trees and cast shadows across the ancient stones carved with scriptures from sacred texts thousands of years old.

The acoustics of the sacred place allowed anyone passing through the courtyard to hear the softly-chanted mantras from the meditation halls surrounding the garden. The sound of two monks chanting inside led Vincent to pause in the doorway of the centuries-old temple's hall, hoping their prayers would bring him solace, insight, and answers. Instead, it took him on an introspective journey.

☥

Vincent had always been a man of faith. He was an active member of his local church and spent much of his time in prayer, seeking guidance through the troubles that filled his life. But recently, he felt weighed down by something invisible, like something was holding him back, preventing him from being truly happy and fulfilled. As time passed, the resentment grew stronger within his heart. He felt as if no one could understand what he was going through or how deeply hurt and broken he was. The longer this went on, the harder it became for him to let go and move forward with his life.

Insidious sadness and a deep shame marked Vincent's childhood. He had experienced so much hurt and suffering at the hands of a trusted family friend that it felt like he walked with an anchor around his neck, weighing him down and making it hard to stay afloat. A close family friend sexually assaulted him, forcing themself upon Vincent multiple times. The memories were hard to shake; his abuser made sure of it with their constant threats and manipulation, making him feel as if he were somehow to blame for the inexcusable acts they had committed.

During those dark times in his childhood, Vincent experienced moments of hopelessness—the anguish and despair seemed almost too much to bear. He often questioned why someone so close would do such a terrible thing, yet he never found a satisfactory answer. The torment of being unable to protect himself from the person who should have been his trusted confidante and protector brought him to tears, reminding him of how powerless he truly felt.

For many years, Vincent attended weekly therapy sessions, trying to make sense of the abuse he had suffered. Despite his best efforts, however, the pain didn't lessen, and nothing seemed to help him cope with the trauma he had endured. He found it difficult to confront the feelings and memories associated with the sexual abuse; every time he thought about it, waves of anger, guilt, and sadness came crashing down.

Vincent struggled between feeling helpless, unable to move past what had happened, and absolutely frustrated that he couldn't put the trauma behind him. His therapist tried to provide guidance and support, but Vincent often felt stuck in a hopeless abyss, unable to find relief. Even when things looked promising, or he opened up more than usual during a session, the heaviness inside would linger long after leaving the therapist's office. Despite all the setbacks and moments of despair, he continued going to therapy week after week with the intention of eventually finding peace within himself—something that seemed just out of reach.

Every morning, Vincent woke up feeling as if he were living two lives: one filled with joy and hope for what the future could bring and a dark one filled with anxiety and fear. The days felt like never-ending cycles of trying to find moments of inner peace while dodging painful reminders of what had happened when he was a young boy.

Because of his shame and the abuser's threats, Vincent never told anyone about the abuse—not even his wife or children—leaving him feeling isolated and alone during the day. No matter how hard he tried to forget the past, the memories still haunted him every day. They crept into his thoughts uninvited and threatened to take over his life. He tried to push away the pain of his past by burying himself in work and distractions, but nothing ever made it go away completely. Each night, he would lay awake for hours, reliving each moment of the abuse in vivid detail until exhaustion finally forced him to sleep.

Vincent tried everything over the years: meditation, religious practices, long walks in nature—anything to help him focus on something other than his traumatic experiences. But it all seemed useless; no matter how much he tried to distract himself or push through it all, those traumatic memories would always come back every night like clockwork.

The guilt consumed Vincent: *Why did this happen to me? Why didn't I speak out sooner? What would my family think if they knew?* So many questions weighed heavily on him as he silently dealt with the pain alone.

☥

As Vincent stood in the doorway of the meditation room, buried in the heavy burden of pain and trauma, a white dove flew towards him, bringing him back to the present. He believed it to be a sign specifically for him, beckoning him toward some unknown truth greater than anything else.

"Beloved one," the monks in the meditation room said in unison. "We know your soul has been broken and troubled, but we will help you find peace." The two robed men walked toward Vincent, holding their hands in front of their bodies, palms upward. "We invite you to come into this sacred space and feel safe here. Let us heal you from within by cleansing your soul."

The monks' words filled the air with comforting energy, and Vincent felt his body relax for the first time in years. The sensation of unconditional love surrounded him, something he'd only experienced around his sisters while growing up in Sicily. Despite the memories he'd been reliving, Vincent knew he could trust the monks and followed them deeper inside the room.

"It is time to begin anew," the monks said as they dressed Vincent in beautiful robes and placed sandals at his feet to step into—a symbol of rebirth.

After receiving the monks' final gift of jewelry—a token of their love and respect for him—Vincent basked in their kindness, feeling it wash over him like a wave of healing energy.

"We bless you with peace and love in your life," the monks said, embracing Vincent's hands in theirs. "May you always remember to be kind to yourself and others, for we are all connected."

As the monks returned to chanting their ancient healing prayer, Vincent felt a deep sense of understanding swell in his heart. He knew he was no longer alone and had people who cared for him. All his pain and struggles were being removed, replaced by a calmness that settled over him like a blanket.

With a newfound understanding and acceptance of himself and his journey, Vincent was ready to take on the world with grace and compassion. With the monks' help, he discovered his inner strength and the courage to help him through troubled times.

"Let go of what no longer serves you so you can make room for new experiences and awaken your highest potential," the monks said. "You must let go of anything from your past that no longer has any relevance. Only then will you be able to find true happiness."

Their words were like a benediction from the universe for Vincent. It reminded him of what the Bible said about letting go:

> Not that I have already obtained this or am already perfect, but I press on to make it my own because Christ Jesus has made me his own. Brothers, I do not consider that I have made it my own. But one thing I do: forgetting what lies behind and straining forward to what lies ahead, I press on toward the goal for the prize of the upward call of God in Christ Jesus (Philippians 3:12-14, ESV).

For too long, Vincent didn't understand the somberness that had pervaded his life, but the monks began to help him realize what it meant. He saw that he had been living a life defined by expectations set upon him by others—expectations that never made sense or felt right in his heart. Every mistake, every trauma, and every failed expectation seemed to sink him further into a pit of despair and hopelessness. He thought back on all the times he had tried his hardest to live up to these expectations, only to fail again and again. The weight of this realization was heavy as he understood that his accomplishments struck him as meaningless even when he did succeed.

Vincent wanted desperately for somebody—anybody— to understand why it was so hard for him. Instead, it seemed that everyone expected more from him than someone in his circumstances should be held responsible for. He wished somebody would recognize how hard it was for him and offer support instead of demanding more from him at his lowest moments.

The monks reminded Vincent that the past was over and he must look forward. A positive energy radiated to him from the monk's prayer as they chanted ancient wisdom with their meditative tones.

"Thank you," he said with deep gratitude and closed his eyes, allowing himself to absorb their blessings and blessing for all humanity.

Vincent opened his eyes to a feeling of inner peace and understanding of life's greater mysteries. The monks continued praying for him until he felt an overwhelming connection with something larger than himself and the weight of the world released from his shoulders.

Suddenly, a strange fog rolled in around Vincent, disrupting the peacefulness of the moment. As he looked away from the monks and peered into the misty afternoon light, he saw all the temples disappearing. Looking back at the monks for an explanation, he witnessed them vanish one by one, leaving only traces of their presence like fading echoes. Nothing remained but emptiness where sacred structures had been standing tall moments prior.

The momentary panic gave way to tears rolling down his cheeks. Vincent mourned the loss while thoughts raced through his mind: *Is this divine intervention? Did I cause this? Is this fate intervening?*

"You are here now because you have chosen to seek enlightenment and stop the suffering not only for yourself but for all humanity," a voice called out to him from high atop a nearby mountain.

Vincent squinted, and although he shouldn't have been able to see that far with such clarity, he saw Jesus standing in solidarity on top of the peak, beckoning Vincent toward him. Without fear or hesitation, he began walking toward Jesus without another glance back at the vacant land. Each step drew him deeper into understanding himself—like an invisible force inviting him forward with a gentle but powerful tug on his spirit. He knew he was there to transform his life.

Step after step, Vincent finally arrived at the summit. While he stood under a sky full of stars, planets, and a full moon glowing brightly above everything, he entered a trance-like state, weakened and falling under a spell cast on him from the heavens above. His body was immovable as if made of stone, yet he drifted off into an entirely different realm.

"Do not fear, my child," a voice said in an otherworldly tone filled with compassion and understanding. Then, the voice quoted Jeremiah 29:11: "For I know the plans I have for you, plans to prosper you and not to harm you, plans to give you hope and a future."

Normally, Vincent would have expected more to be said, but he was content with these simple words and laid down on the patch of grass beneath his feet. As he gazed up at the stars, his thoughts slowly drifted until he was soundly sleeping, dreaming of a future filled with possibility. The starlight blanketed him in solace and peace as Vincent's mind carried him to a world of hope and possibilities that night.

Chapter Seven

…so in Christ we, though many, form one body,
and each member belongs to all the others.

—Romans 12:5

The calming presence of the moon gave way to the warm morning sun, and Vincent slowly awoke from his dream-filled sleep feeling refreshed and content—the night had been transformative. As he stretched and got his bearings, Vincent felt something stir inside him: determination. He hadn't felt that since he moved from Sicily with only hope in his heart despite spending years searching for something—anything—that could give him that same feeling of hope and ambition.

As he descended the mountain, Vincent felt blessed to have experienced such a magical night and hoped to cherish it for as long as he lived. However, as the scenery shifted around him, so did the skies above. Blue gave way to gray, and soon rain beat against him in relentless waves. His determination lacked direction, and his hope began to wane. It felt like a metaphor for his life: Pleasure was short-lived.

Soaked and disoriented, Vincent was lost in his thoughts and the terrain. One foot squished in front of the other on the muddy path, and occasionally he stopped to look around, desperate for a familiar landmark to guide him back home. The further he went, the more panic filled his chest.

It seemed like hours had passed before the pressure began to subside: a glimmer of hope appeared ahead of Vincent in the form of a glowing yellow light emanating from deep within the jungle. Mesmerized by its warmth and beauty, he followed it to a small hut. The building was otherworldly in appearance, so he touched the exterior wall—bamboo and palm fronds woven together with feathers and seashells to create intricate designs—to make sure he wasn't hallucinating. Topped by a conical-shaped roof made of thatched reeds, he decided retreating inside would be a welcome reprise from the rain.

The external size was deceiving. As Vincent entered the hidden retreat, a welcoming aroma of herbs and spices greeted him. A colorful tapestry depicting scenes from ancient mythology hung from one wall while a fire pit in the middle of the room released smoke toward a ceiling adorned with twinkling stars. Some guests sat around the room, telling each other tales about days gone by in the ambiance of flickering candles. Others basked in their thoughts beside the warmth of the fire pit.

Vincent started toward the central fire, hoping to dry off. The breeze gently blowing inside should have made him shiver. Instead, it felt comforting, like spirits were living inside the walls, watching over all the guests, keeping them safe.

As he approached the fire, Vincent was met by a woman with kind, knowing eyes. She welcomed him into her home—which surprised him because it felt more like a resort—and offered him a blanket and a cup of hot tea.

"I don't mean to intrude," Vincent said, sitting on the bench near the fire the woman gestured toward. "I'm not sure how or why I'm here."

There was a long silence as the woman stared at Vincent with her warm, chestnut-colored eyes, smiling. His anxiety shifted, and he began to relax while studying his host, who seemed to have the heart of an angel and a smile that could melt any soul. The woman's light-flowing hair that framed her face like a halo added to the feeling that he was sharing that space with a magical, divine being.

"I am Mother Earth," the woman began. "I am nature. The divine in the sun, stars, wind, and rain, and all of life flows through me."

Bewildered, Vincent blinked as he tried to wrap his brain around this introduction.

Seeing his expression, the woman smiled. "You may call me Olivia."

Vincent released a sigh of relief. "Olivia," he whispered. He felt that Olivia had been sent from the heavens above. He knew she was there to teach him a valuable lesson.

"Outdoors is full of life, energy, infinite beauty, and awe, where nature creates a symphony with its diversity. It's brimming with life, energy, and vibrancy, a living, breathing ecosystem filled with creatures, large and small. The birds sing to the trees that stand steadfastly like sentinels in the sky, and the creeks ripple invitingly toward us. We can feel the sun's warmth on our faces as we take time to value all the natural wonders around us.

"Taking moments to appreciate this beauty reminds us of our interconnectedness with nature and that, despite its wildness, it brings us solace and peace. Our connection to nature is eternal and will never be forgotten or broken. Nature is our home and will always be full of life and energy."

Olivia stood and motioned Vincent to follow her. The two walked down a hallway that led to a porch with a view of the jungle. After settling into deck chairs, someone brought a cup of tea for each of them and quietly left them to their conversation.

After taking a long sip of her tea while gazing at the scenery, Olivia continued. "The outdoors is a reminder of the raw beauty that exists in our world—an ode to the power of nature. Its ever-changing scenes can evoke deep admiration, wonderment, and joy within us if we allow it. Each day brings new discoveries and moments of connection as we explore its depths. In this way, nature provides a backdrop for our lives, enhancing them with its vibrant colors and sounds.

"As we reconnect with nature, we can feel the sheer magnitude of energy radiating from all around us. Every creature on land and sea plays its part in creating this bustling atmosphere, filling us with hope and a sense of curiosity. Can you feel the overwhelming sensation of life, energy, and exhilaration permeating the air?"

Olivia's wisdom spoke to Vincent's soul. He felt tingles all over his body and deeply inhaled the fresh air as he nodded in reply.

"The outdoors is full of vitality and purpose; it's a place to explore, learn from, and be inspired by." Olivia squinted at something in the distance. "Though it may seem chaotic and unpredictable at times, it is truly a testament to the beauty and resilience of nature. Its wildness speaks to us in ways that words alone cannot describe; its energy gives us hope for a brighter future. Whether taking time out for ourselves or simply enjoying its wonders with loved ones, the outdoors will always remain full of life and energy."

Silence fell between the two again, which allowed Vincent to listen to the sounds of nature surrounding them. It felt like Olivia was part of nature, speaking for it, so when she broke the silence, it didn't startle him.

"Native Americans praise the beauty of this land, often referring to it as a gift from the Great Spirit. They revere its diversity: its majestic mountains and lush valleys, vibrant sunrises and starry nights. Yet, there is an underlying sense of sadness when they speak of the beauty in nature, describing it as 'laden with tears' because of the sorrows of those who hadn't been about to protect their sacred land from exploitation. Their stories are part of our shared history, reminding us of what once was and what could be again." Olivia closed her eyes, and a single tear rolled down her cheek.

Vincent felt inspired. So as Olivia sat in quiet meditation, he added to her words. "Even though the land has changed, its beauty remains. People can still be awed by the magnificence of her mountains, captivated by her diverse wildlife, and inspired by her breathtaking sunrises and sunsets."

Olivia turned to Vincent and smiled. "Despite our differences and the trials we face in life, and no matter how far apart or what lies between us, this majestic land bonds and unites us. It's a collective responsibility to honor its history while cherishing its beauty." She took Vincent's hand and bowed her head in prayer. "Let us embrace Her spirit and strive to make the world better for everyone. May we continue to be blessed by the Great Spirit with this beautiful land that unites us all in awe, respect, and joy."

Although her prayer was uplifting, Olivia's words provoked guilt inside Vincent. "I've wasted so much time indoors, medicating myself with television, the internet, and other toxins. I feel how much they've destroyed me," he confessed as he withdrew his hand from hers and looked down.

Olivia gently lifted his chin to meet her eyes, then rested her hand on his shoulder. "I have something that can heal you." With that, she transformed into a figure made entirely of light, glowing like a full moon on the darkest night.

Soundless words entered Vincent's mind. *Traditional medicines cannot cure all illnesses. But being outdoors has healing powers. Connect deeply with Nature. Listen carefully to its sounds and feel its energy beneath your skin. By grounding yourself within Nature's embrace, you will absorb its positive energy, restoring balance to your life.*

Vincent felt Olivia's deep wisdom of many lifetimes. As he started to speak, the light transformed back into the woman he had first met. The transformation was so beautiful it left him speechless.

"Do not forget the power of Nature, Vincent. Her beauty has a way of healing in ways that words cannot explain," Oliva said, her gaze meeting his eyes again. "Take time to get out into her arms and be still so you can feel your connection with all life. The solace it brings will fill your heart with peace."

"Thank you," Vincent said as Olivia bestowed her blessing on him. The words fell short of the gratitude he felt, but with no other words coming to mind, he bowed his head to her and returned inside.

As Vincent exited the hidden retreat, he reflected on Olivia's teachings. He embraced the sense of love emanating from all around him, even from plants and trees that nor-mally seemed so distant and unapproachable. It was like they were feeling something beyond their physical forms, something intangible yet strangely familiar to him.

An eerie silence of nightfall surrounded Vincent as he walked through the jungle. He sensed voices calling out to him, somber tones belonging to all the great warriors of the past. As they echoed through the darkness, he was reminded that life was both beautiful and mysterious. Even though this strange land was peaceful, something was unsettling about it. Every time Vincent tried to make sense of what was happening or figure out which direction his life should go next, he felt a fog cloud his senses, making it difficult for him to distinguish reality from fiction.

By the time he reached the cottage, the sounds of night surrounded Vincent. But his walk back had left him feeling that everything in his life wasn't enough for him anymore. He wanted more clarity on what lay ahead. There was so much potential waiting just beyond his reach. So, after taking a deep, cleansing breath, he passed by the casita and continued onward.

Chapter Eight

Be very careful, then, how you live—not as unwise but as wise,
making the most of every opportunity...

—Ephesians 5:15-16

V incent walked all night. Time seemed to slow down, but
eventually, dawn leisurely came. He had been thinking
about how lost in life he felt, stuck in a cycle of stress
and unhappiness. He lived in the hustle and bustle of
modern life with no reprieve from its chaotic pace.

As he continued his unspecified journey, Vincent sensed
an unfamiliar presence following him. With all he'd experienced in this strange land, he knew it had to be another
spiritual guide calling out to him. Despite his internal
turmoil, he felt strangely at peace and comforted by this
mysterious entity. Just like in the previous days, he knew

this would be the start of another journey toward understanding himself.

Vincent felt led toward a path taking him deep into the jungle, and he hoped it would be closer to some hidden truth. With each step he took, he felt closer to a stronger sense of clarity. Even though he didn't know the destination, Vincent anticipated it would bring him enlightenment.

Reminded of his lessons the previous day, Vincent looked around in awe as he walked silently through dense trees, connecting with nature. Every blade of grass and each rustling leaf felt like it held a secret waiting to be revealed. The occasional sun rays sparkling off everything they touched reminded him that although things change quickly, nature remains constant.

Finally, he arrived at a tranquil meadow surrounded by trees filled with birds singing sweet melodies, creating a magical atmosphere. The whispers of his unseen guide continued pulling him forward until he reached an oak tree in the heart of the clearing.

"Slow down. Where are you going in such a hurry?" the voice—no longer a whisper—asked.

As Vincent looked around and saw no one, he decided to sit beneath the tree to reflect on the question. He felt further away from his true self and stuck in the hurriedness of his life. It wasn't just him, though.

Vincent had experienced the glitz and glamour of cities, the chaos of traffic, and people scurrying around like ants just trying to earn their living. From bustling cities to small villages deep in the mountains, he had experienced many different cultures and lifestyles. Yet no matter where he went, one thing remained constant: life was always busy. People worked long hours to make ends meet; children struggled under heavy workloads at school; families rarely found time for quality time . . . . Everywhere he looked, people were rushing to get somewhere. *Why? What's the end goal? Why does life have to be so hectic and stressful?*

The need to slow down the pace of his life suddenly consumed Vincent. He was exhausted from running a race where he didn't know what the finish line looked like. Overwhelmed by the feeling of being lost, he felt frustrated by the ever-changing world that seemed so determined to have him keep up with the elusive clock.

"Life is about the moment and memories you create," the voice said, interrupting Vincent's thoughts. "Instead of striving for fame, fortune, and material possessions, shift your focus to creating meaningful experiences with your loved ones."

Vincent looked around but still didn't see who was speaking to him.

His guide continued to depart wisdom. "People are often too caught up in the rat race of life that they forget to appreciate the beauty around them. Take a step back and recognize what's most important: relationships, making genuine connections with others, and self-discovery of who you are as an individual."

In the back of Vincent's mind, he wondered who his mysterious guide was. But his thoughts were forced to recall times when life was simpler, when days weren't consumed by rushing around. "Time moved slower then," Vincent said, knowing that his guide could see the thoughts in his mind.

"Everyone wants more from their lives. But that comes at the expense of having less time to fulfill themselves. The world isn't spinning faster than before; people are moving faster through life," the voice said.

An awareness that this was affecting his life dawned on Vincent. He had always been full of ambition: from his side hustle in the streets of Sicily as a kid to struggling to "make it" on the foreign shores of New York as a teenager to rising high in his career as an adult. His ambition drove him, demanding he become the best at everything he did, no matter how grueling it was. He was eager to get ahead and achieve more than he already had.

It was Vincent's ambition, though, that often made him rush through his days, never taking the time to enjoy the moments. He was always moving, always trying to make something out of nothing. It often felt like he was sprinting at high speed toward his death.

As the years ticked by, this feeling intensified. As Vincent's goals became more unrealistic, he took bigger risks to get things done faster: skipping meals, working longer hours with less sleep, pushing himself through exhaustion to accomplish one goal, and not recovering before he started on the next. Working on projects until late in the night, refusing to rest until he had done more than expected, his ambition had pushed him to the limit and beyond—at a high price.

"Your quest for success has cost you dearly," the guide interjected.

As the self-inflicted pressure to achieve his goals increased, Vincent's wife and children felt the strain. His work consumed most of his time, energy, and attention, leaving little to give to his family.

"The happiness of everyone I love," Vincent replied. "The more I've focused on achieving things, the more the most important things in my life have slipped away. My wife feels neglected, and I've lost my connection with my daughters." The stress of this realization weighed heavily on his heart.

Vincent's laser focus on achieving more also took a heavy toll on him. A lack of balance coupled with insomnia, a poor diet, and the inability to relax affected him physically and mentally. This dangerous cycle of stress and exhaustion would eventually lead to losing everything.

"Why are you unable to stop and appreciate the beauty of the life you have?" the guide asked. Without waiting for a response, he continued. "You race from one task to the next with little regard for yourself or others. And what do you gain? Stress and fractured relationships." There was no judgment in the guide's words—just truth.

"I'm on the brink of burnout," Vincent admitted. "But how do I change? How do I regain balance?"

The guide answered by showing Vincent how his ambition had hurt those around him. He felt the disappointment of the people who loved him as they watched him race from one goal to the next. Images of people he could have connected with and helped, along with opportunities that would've made him happy, flashed through Vincent's mind in the visions the guide shared.

Tears rolled down Vincent's cheeks, and he felt the sharp sting of guilt. "I've hurt so many people. I have to slow down and make time for others. I need to do things that make me happy too." The Bible verse Philippians 4:6-7 went through his mind: *Do not be anxious about anything, but in every situation, by prayer and petition, with thanksgiving, present your requests to God. And the peace of God, which transcends all understanding, will guard your hearts and your minds in Christ Jesus (NIV)*. It reminded Vincent to slow down, enjoy the moment, and remember that God was always watching over him.

The guide spoke again. "Mark 8:36 says, 'What will it profit a man if he gains the whole world but loses his soul?' If you prioritize worldly accomplishments over peace and faith, you get lost in a cycle of stress and worry, overcome by the desperate need for gain. Jesus did not want this for us."

Vincent remembered when life was simpler: the days didn't involve rushing around, and time moved slower. That's when he realized why life felt so busy nowadays—because it was! Everyone wanted more from their lives, which meant having less time for themselves or others; something had changed drastically. The world wasn't spinning faster than before, but people were moving more quickly through it.

"I don't want to lose my soul," Vincent said.

"When you prioritize worldly accomplishments over peace and faith, you will find yourself lost in this cycle of stress and worry, consumed, as you are, by the desperate need for gain. This isn't what Jesus wants for you. If you don't slow down and reconnect with your faith, your life will continue to be full of regrets like the ones you feel now."

The lessons the guide was teaching Vincent were simple but profound, and he was eager to learn more.

"You must strive to be in alignment with your higher self, Vincent, and to remain unruffled by the situations and people around you," Vincent's spirit guide said.

"How do I do that?" Vincent cocked his head to the side, unsure how to do what was asked of him.

"Pay attention to your breathing," the guide said.

This seemed like a strange response, but Vincent complied, resting his back against the tree.

"It's important to focus on your breathing to obtain the meditative state necessary to receive spiritual guidance. Now, take a deep breath, filling your lungs with air until your entire body is filled with it."

Vincent inhaled deeply, his chest and head rising as air filled him.

"Do not hold your breath, though," the guide instructed Vincent. "Breathe normally, focusing on the sound of your breathing. With each breath, clear your mind of distracting thoughts and feelings. Replace them with feelings of peace and tranquility."

With a nod of understanding, Vincent's chest deflated, and he began to breathe normally.

"Close your eyes, Vincent, and concentrate on nothing but the rhythm of your breaths." The guide paused to allow Vincent to get into a cadence of deep breathing. "You are more open to receiving wisdom and insight from a higher source when you enter this meditative state. With practice, you can eventually reach the highest levels of spiritual awareness and get closer to your true self."

As Vincent focused on his deep breaths, he became aware of the presence of spiritual energy surrounding him. The more he tried to connect with it, though, the farther it got. Finally, Vincent opened his eyes and sighed.

Sensing Vincent's frustration, the guide said, "It takes time, but you must react to this and all situations without judgment. You will need to practice this regularly to achieve its full benefits. Your skills will become more refined, leading you further down your spiritual path. When you are aligned with yourself, you become unaffected by the people and situations around you. But you must be patient with yourself, Vincent. With dedication, you will reach the divine state of blissful contemplation."

Vincent nodded, closed his eyes again, and continued breathing.

"Do not allow yourself to be fooled by outward appearances or driven by your biases. See people for who they truly are: flawed human beings just like you. Everyone is on their own journey of self-discovery and growth. Remain open, compassionate, and accepting of others regardless of how they act or what they say."

"Unconditional love," Vincent whispered. He started to understand how to take each situation in stride and learn something from every encounter. It was a way for him to be more mindful and resilient when he faced challenges.

"Yes. And when you respond from a place of equanimity rather than emotion or opinion, you will remain true to yourself and grow spiritually. Lead with an open heart, Vincent."

The feeling of the guide disappeared, and Vincent opened his eyes and felt inner peace. He listened to the wind whisper secrets of the wild across the orange and pink sky. It felt like a magical blanket caressed the world, filling the air with awe-inspiring energy that drew him closer to nature's mysterious beauty. In the distance, a chorus of birds sang farewell to the sun as dusk descended upon the land.

Stillness remained in Vincent as the sky glittered with stars and the moon. He basked in the peace and overwhelming connection with nature he felt. And while his mysterious sage had left, he heard the wise man's words in his mind: "No matter how dark the world is, there will always be something to keep you going."

Something changed inside Vincent that day. He gained a newfound appreciation for every moment in life, big or small, and knew he could take solace in the fact that all moments mattered.

Vincent slowly walked back to his casita with an appreciation for the need to understand the power of now. He'd shifted into a different world that day, one that would remain with him forever. Anxiety began dissipating, replaced by an inner peace that left him feeling more grounded than ever. The once hurried lifestyle now felt slower yet far more meaningful as he vowed to savor each moment for everything it offered instead of rushing through them blindly so he could finish his race faster.

The light from the casita was like a beacon in the night, welcoming Vincent home after his long journey. The wind whispered invitingly to him as it moved through the trees and caressed his face, giving him the breath he needed to face whatever was on the path ahead of him.

As he crossed the threshold, Vincent took comfort in his cozy surroundings and the newfound knowledge that hope can be found in the small moments in life. Those moments allow time to appreciate the beauty of life and all it has to offer.

Vincent settled into bed and thanked the Universe for this momentary respite. More than ever, he appreciated that beauty and light could be found even in the darkest times. Exhausted from the emotional events of the day yet feeling more content and peaceful than ever, Vincent drifted off to sleep.

Chapter Nine

*Children's children are a crown to the aged, and parents
are the pride of their children.*

—Proverbs 17:6

Luca and Cecilia's Story

Luca was a mysterious little boy with deep dark eyes and
unruly black hair. He had an aura of beauty about him
that made it hard for those who encountered him to look
away. His family lived in the heart of a mystical jungle, their
home surrounded by tall trees and lush foliage that reached
toward the sky like fingers grasping for something more.

The jungle held many secrets, some of which Luca
wished he could uncover. Every day, he went into its depths,
armed only with curiosity and courage. As he explored

further and further into the unknown, strange creatures began to appear before him: giant tree-dwelling spiders and mischievous monkeys playing tricks on unsuspecting travelers. He even heard rumors of people seeing dragons.

Despite these dangers, Luca never gave up his explorations. Somehow, they filled his soul with joy as if this was what he was meant to do—discover hidden mysteries no one else could see or understand.

Cecilia, Lucas's younger sister, was the light of his life. Despite her youth, Cecilia had a wisdom that belied her age. She carried herself with a quiet confidence that spoke of experience and maturity, and her words were always measured and thoughtful. Her insights were often profound, and she had a way of making you see things in a new light. When she spoke, people listened. There was a grace and poise to her manner that drew others to her, and she had a natural charisma that made her stand out in any crowd. However, Cecilia was not one to seek attention, but it seemed to find her anyway, drawn to her like a magnet.

But what really set Cecilia apart was her kind heart. She had a generosity of spirit that touched everyone she met and was always there to lend a helping hand or a sympathetic ear. Her compassion and empathy were genuine, and she had a way of making you feel seen and heard, no matter who you were.

☥

Vincent contemplated the lessons he had learned the previous day and embraced the concept of slowing down as he walked through the trees. He was admiring the birds' songs when he heard children laughing. Curious about what lessons children might have for him—lessons can be taught by people of any age, young or old—he walked in the direction the sound was coming from.

Before Vincent saw them, Luca and Cecilia popped out from behind a tree and hesitantly walked toward him. When the two were in front of him, they both squinted and looked into his eyes like they were expecting something.

Vincent's face transformed with sorrow and pain. He knew why they had come—to find peace within himself.

Tilting his head side to side, Luca said, "Family, friends, and joy are important no matter what."

Cecilia nodded enthusiastically, encouraging Vincent to listen to the truths her brother spoke of.

Vincent offered a half-smile and shrugged. There was no way for children to understand the burdens he carried. But there was something about Cecilia's presence that comforted him.

"Family is one of the most precious gifts in life," Cecilia said. Like her brother's, her voice was like the sound of angels offering him a chance for redemption. "There is nothing like having someone always there to love, support, and understand you no matter what."

"Having a family means having people who know your story, who are connected to you through shared experiences and memories." Luca paused to smile at Cecilia. "It's a feeling of security that can never be replicated by anyone or anything else."

Vincent was awed by the maturity of the children and how seamlessly they expanded on each other's ideas. He decided not to interrupt their flow.

"Knowing your family will still be there for you through every twist and turn of life brings a deep comfort that many take for granted," Cecilia said.

"Without family, our lives would feel significantly emptier and colder," Luca added matter-of-factly. "It's an irreplaceable source of unconditional love that helps us get through any difficulty we may encounter."

Vincent nodded in agreement. "Family is one of the greatest blessings I've received," he admitted.

Luca and Cecilia nodded enthusiastically.

"It gives a sense of belonging, understanding, and guidance unlike anything else," Luca said, squeezing his sister's hand.

Cecilia giggled and nodded. "Yes, so make sure you cherish moments with your family and build strong relationships with them so you can experience all the joy that comes with having a strong family bond."

"Family makes life worth living, so don't take them for granted," Luca advised.

Cecilia nodded in agreement. "You know, family isn't just about blood. Family can be anyone who loves and supports you, who's there for you no matter what. It's about building strong relationships, creating a sense of belonging, and being part of something bigger than yourself." Then, she leaned forward like she was going to share a secret, her eyes sparkling with warmth. "And you don't have to do it alone. We're here for you, Vincent. We'll help and support you every step of the way," she whispered.

"Yeah," Luca agreed. "We've learned to appreciate the little things in life with our family. It's not about how much money you make or how many possessions you have. It's about the experiences you have and the people you share them with."

Vincent realized how much he had lost sight of that. "I hear you. Lately, it feels like all I do is work and worry about the future. I've forgotten how to just be present and enjoy the moment."

Cecilia put her hand on his arm. "Vincent, I think we all get caught up in that sometimes. People are taught to strive for success and accumulate wealth and possessions from a young age. But at the end of the day, none of those matter. What matters is the people in your life, your family, and friends."

"I remember when my grandfather was dying," Luca said. "He told me that at the end of your life, family is all that matters. It's not about how much money you have or how many awards you've won. The love you share with others is the only important thing."

Vincent stared off into the distance, his heart heavy with remorse. He had neglected his family for too long while pursuing earthly possessions that meant nothing to him now. His wife and children had been left behind as he chased after what he thought would make him happy—a bigger house, fancier cars, more expensive clothes—but it was all so meaningless; none of these things could bring him joy when his family wasn't there to share them with him.

Happy memories with his family flashed through Vincent's mind. He thought about his wife and children and how much they meant to him. Simple things like his daughters' faces lighting up when they opened presents on birthdays or holidays and how excited they got when going out for ice cream together. Even just watching them play in the backyard made Vincent smile fondly.

Vincent remembered all the times they had laughed together, cried together, and supported each other through thick and thin. He knew his family was his rock, his anchor, his reason for living. And yet, he had been neglecting them lately, putting work and other things ahead of them. All those moments were lost because of his selfishness and ambition.

The tears began streaming down Vincent's face as he thought about all that could have been if he hadn't taken every opportunity away from them by chasing money instead of spending time with them like he should have done. He vowed never to take another moment for granted again—this time, nothing would come before his family.

Cecilia offered Vincent a tissue with a soft smile. "You can make the future better," she said.

With those final words, Cecilia and Luca disappeared into the thick trees they came from.

Vincent watched the children skip away with happiness in their hearts and was deeply moved by their message. As he walked away, he thought about what Luca and Cecilia had said about the importance of family and the love and connection that sustained us through life's ups and downs.

He knew that he had to make changes in his life, starting with his priorities. The most important things Vincent made a mental note about were spending more quality time with his family, being there for them when they needed him, and showing them how much he loved and appreciated them. He knew it wouldn't be easy, but he was determined to make it happen and vowed to make up for lost time by being fully present with them in every moment.

Chapter Ten

*You make known to me the path of life; you will fill me with joy
in your presence, with eternal pleasures at your right hand.*

—Psalm 16:11

A fter another night of peaceful sleep, Vincent opened
his eyes to greet another day and, hopefully, another
experience that would bring more enlightenment. His
blurry eyes slowly focused on his room, now adorned with
artifacts. Colorful masks, feathers, and intricate carvings,
along with healing herbs, stones, and talismans decorated
the inside of the casita. As he leaned forward to examine
them, he thought he heard their whispers of ancient wisdom.

The energy in his room was powerful and calming.
Vincent knew there were forces around him at work that
were far greater than human understanding. His casita had

become a portal to the spiritual realm, and he felt invited to surrender to the mystery of it and explore its innermost depths without judgment or expectation.

As he rose from the bed to engage with the spiritual objects, Vincent wondered what stories they would share and what secrets they'd reveal. The artifacts were not only symbols of the past but an invitation to explore the future, both spiritually and creatively. One of the iridescent feathers called more strongly to him, so he carried it to the bed, laying down as he held it over him to study it closer.

Suddenly, Vincent froze, unable to speak or move. The pervasive calm atmosphere of the room prevented him from panicking, but it didn't stop him from wondering why it was happening and what was to come. As his mind raced with questions, a bright light flickering outside his window caught his attention. Was it a spirit trying to communicate with him?

The wind carried the angelic voice of a woman from the light to Vincent. The language was unfamiliar to him, possibly Latin, but it was unlike anything he'd ever heard. The words he couldn't understand were comforting to him, yet delivered with a firm tone. They swirled around the room until one word reverberated: Vincent.

If he had been able to move, Vincent would've shot upright in the bed. As his eyes darted around, he felt the paralysis ease and sat up to face the mysterious light that had entered his room.

"I am the goddess of truth," the luminous being said. "You may call me Elaina. I am here to give you the most sacred wisdom if you choose to seek it."

As it said those words, the light transformed into a woman wearing a brightly-colored mask, a work of art intricately crafted and colored in the traditional motifs of a beautiful ceremony. Rings of red, yellow, and green—the colors of life and prosperity—swirled around her face in geometric shapes. It symbolized her commitment to the ceremony, respect for its ancient rituals, and desire to find greater understanding.

While the mask gave the goddess a somber presence, Vincent saw an immense internal strength. It reminded him that everyone has something special within them. "I wish to seek your wisdom," he said.

"My message is that knowledge comes from within. No one else can give you your truth, Vincent," the goddess began. "You cannot rely on what society teaches you or believe in false information received externally. Instead, you must look deep into yourself and search for answers by exploring your thoughts and feelings."

Vincent's forehead creased in confusion. "How can I trust my thoughts and feelings? Don't external situations trigger them?"

"Throughout your life," Elaina began, "I have whispered intuition to you, providing insights that would enlighten you to the truth beyond the physical world. But you have to be still and listen."

Vincent opened his mouth to protest, but his voice was quieted.

"And I will continue to do this, Vincent. You will see me manifest as visions or dreams containing symbols and messages meant to guide you. They are a reminder that the truth lies within you. But it's up to you to discover that truth." Elaina paused, seeing Vincent grapple with her wisdom. "Have patience with yourself. I will help you find your way on your journey toward self-discovery. Now, close your eyes."

A pressure rose in Vincent's chest. All the years of hiding and burying truths from others and himself weighed on him, making it difficult to breathe. But he followed Elaina's instructions and closed his eyes while he pressed his palms on his thighs to stop them from shaking.

"The journey of truth-seeking is often difficult," Elaina commented. "But I can help make it more manageable. With your eyes closed, be mindful of your thoughts and emotions. Through this mindfulness, you will be able to navigate through the ups and downs of life with grace and courage. Next, recognize your unique gifts and embrace a sense of connection with all beings."

Vincent began to relax, but he felt immense guilt for the harm he'd done to others.

Elaina spoke to his anxiety. "Being honest and telling the truth, even after being deceitful, is an essential part of making things right. It can be difficult to come clean about a lie, especially if it has caused harm or hurt someone else."

A tear rolled down Vincent's cheek as he thought about the hurt he'd caused his wife and daughters.

"However," Elaina continued, "having the courage to admit your mistake and take responsibility can help restore trust in others and yourself. Vincent, you will learn a valuable lesson when you accept your mistakes and commit to being truthful."

Vincent knew this was an opportunity for transformation. He could see the light of peace waiting if he could accept and speak his truth. This was an opportunity to heal his soul and bring balance back to his life. But something was holding him back. He remembered all the times he'd been dishonest and felt a wave of regret wash over him.

There had been so many lies Vincent had told throughout his life, and each felt like a lead weight bearing down on him. He thought about all the people he had hurt by telling them untruths and felt ashamed. With every lie, he had betrayed a person's trust in him, damaging their sense of security. In lying to them, he disregarded their feelings as if they weren't worthy enough of his truth.

"It can be difficult to tell the truth when you feel wronged," Elaina explained. "I know you've felt it was easier to retaliate and lash out with lies and half-truths in those moments. But this is not the way. Instead, I invite you to take a moment to understand why you feel hurt and angry."

"By taking deep breaths and focusing on my truths?" Vincent asked.

"Yes," Elaina said, and Vincent could feel her approving smile. "Once you have done that, you will have the strength to tell your story honestly without blame or malice. You can stand up for yourself without compromising your integrity or being deceitful. Even in dishonesty, there is always a way forward with the truth."

"But how? I've damaged relationships because I broke trust. Can these be rebuilt once the trust is shattered?" Vincent thought about all the lies he'd told. At first, they were white lies that seemed insignificant—fibs to make himself look better or stories to make him appear interesting. But as time went on, even the small lies had consequences. As his web of deceit expanded, others began to distrust him. People stopped believing what he said and began questioning his character. No one turned to him for an honest answer or opinion anymore.

"When you tell the truth, your words become infused with love and can have an uplifting effect on others around you. You can inspire others to be their best selves when you practice honesty. In these moments of truth, you will better understand your humanity and the potential that lies within others."

Vincent breathed a sigh of relief at hearing Elaina's advice. He knew the power of truth but had avoided it for so long. Something shifted inside him, though, when the goddess suggested that he could create a positive reputation for himself by speaking his truth. The weight pressing against his chest lifted slightly, and he opened his eyes and sat to face her.

The Goddess of Truth looked at him with her wise eyes filled with compassion and understanding. Vincent felt she could see through to his soul and feel his remorse. "It is time to start telling the truth, Vincent. It won't be easy, but it will be worth it."

Vincent was filled with awe and humility as Elaina spoke to him. Her words were like honey, sweet and comforting yet powerfully insightful. He knew she was right, that truth had the power to create a feeling of unity between all people despite their differences. Moreover, it could bring about a kind of understanding and connection that most people would never know otherwise.

These thoughts extended beyond Vincent, and he felt immense sorrow knowing how much pain lies and deceit had caused throughout human history. He looked deep within himself for courage and strength to begin his journey towards truth-telling, hoping he could be part of creating something beautiful in this world by bringing peace through honesty.

Once again, Elaina smiled at Vincent. "You are destined to make an impact on humanity. But this will require you to be brave and believe in yourself to speak your truth. You are ready to begin your journey toward true connection and understanding and to create unity with the world through honesty." With that final blessing, she transformed back into radiant light and moved across the pink and orange sky toward the setting sun.

Vincent watched as she floated toward the horizon until the sunlight engulfed her. Elaina had given Vincent a way to move forward, but he had a lot to think about. He returned to laying in his bed, his thoughts full of the beautiful advice the Goddess of Truth had gifted him.

Chapter Eleven

Do not conform to the pattern of this world,
but be transformed by the renewing of your mind.

—Romans 12:2

A new day dawned, and Vincent felt some trepidation as he stepped into the warm morning light. He had already seen and learned so much. What would this day bring? He paused and closed his eyes to bask in the sunlight, awaiting his next adventure.

The sounds of nature surrounding him gave Vincent the sense of a deep connection to something larger than himself. As he opened his eyes and gazed at the light blue sky, he longed for something more, like an electric energy in the air was beckoning him toward another journey.

As Vincent followed the invisible pull, his anxiety eased. "No matter where this path leads," he said, "I am ready to embrace it." He continued on his walk with peaceful determination, ready to discover whatever awaited him.

The sun rose higher in the sky, allowing Vincent to view the horizon without squinting. Surprisingly, amid the vastness of nature surrounding it stood a large temple, different from the ones he'd encountered already in this strange land. As he approached, his neck craned to gaze at the walls that seemed to reach beyond the sky. A warm glow emanated from the walls, making the structure feel like a beacon guiding weary travelers from the darkness.

Upon entering, Vincent ran his fingers along the intricate carvings that decorated the internal walls as his eyes scanned the offerings of fruits, vegetables, and incense placed around the room. Despite the room's stillness, the energy within the temple made the hair on his arms stand on end.

The air was thick with smoke from the incense, yet Vincent detected a figure cutting through the haze to enter the room. Standing before him was a monk whose gaze held the weight of a million years. His ancient eyes looked as if they had witnessed stories that only he knew the truth of. Vincent felt he was standing in the presence of something divine, with a daunting yet calming presence.

"Welcome, Vincent," the monk said. "I am Ethaniel." He motioned with a slight nod for Vincent to follow him deeper into the temple.

At once, Vincent felt connected to something deeper when Ethaniel spoke. He was partaking in a timeless conversation between souls from different eras. Although this experience was beyond his comprehension, his heart swelled with anticipation as he walked beside the monk.

A faint melody grew louder as the two walked through the temple hallways until they arrived at a large wooden door. Vincent stared at it in awe—the door seemed alive because of the light emanating from it.

Ethaniel opened it. "Now is the time for you to come into alignment with the divine."

Something stirred within Vincent, and he stepped into a place both magical and intimidating. The room was an expansive temple chamber lit by hundreds of candles that emitted an ethereal light. Everywhere he looked, Vincent saw symbols and artwork from ancient cultures. In the center, a large altar for prayers was the focal point, surrounded by statues of gods and goddesses from times long gone. He felt the solemn grandeur of great power and authority representing the divine will of the heavens in human form while the music spoke directly to his soul.

Ethaniel silently stepped beside Vincent and placed a hand on his shoulder. "You hold within you all the answers you seek," he said in a soft but powerful voice. "Let your spirit be guided to its truest potential. This is where you will find all that you need."

As if by instinct, Vincent understood the power of those words, and his spirit opened up to something deeper, something greater than the Universe itself. He realized that Ethaniel was telling him to be true to find his authentic self. "Yes," Vincent said as he turned to look at the monk.

Ethaniel looked at Vincent with solemn eyes, his voice thick with mysticism. "You will face a great challenge," he said. "No one can truly be their authentic self in this world. There are too many obstacles, too many false paths, too many distractions."

He paused for a moment before continuing. "But you must remain faithful to yourself above all else. That is your only path to genuine fulfillment and joy." With a simple gesture, Ethaniel grasped Vincent's hands. "Listen to your inner voice. Follow your intuition. This is the only path to lead you to discover who you truly are."

Vincent closed his eyes and bowed his head. The warmth of Ethaniel's touch spread throughout his body. "Yes," he whispered and knew the wisdom of the monk's words had imprinted on his soul. He would carry them with him as a guide through life's challenges and the path of discovering who he was meant to be.

"Take time for stillness and reflection. This is essential to help you hear the whispers of your soul. Only then will you be able to recognize what is important in your life and how best to live it out," Ethaniel advised. "Listen carefully. Listen deeply."

This promise Ethaniel offered, one of no greater revelation than the one he could uncover within, resonated with Vincent. The silence in the room seemed to whisper more insights, telling him to trust himself and allow his true self to emerge with grace, courage, and integrity.

"Your true self has been hidden away for too long, Vincent," Ethaniel said. "It's time to free yourself from expectations. Be brave enough to embrace your unique gifts."

"Embrace who I'm meant to be," Vincent said, opening his eyes.

"And allow that knowledge to illuminate your path forward," Ethaniel added. "The most important thing you can do is to spend time figuring out your beliefs. It is not an easy journey, but it will lead to a better understanding of who you are and why you exist on this earth."

Vincent thought about this for a moment. "I need to figure out what I want out of life."

"And say no to everything else," the monk said with a smile. "Your beliefs will guide you through life's challenges and open your mind to possibilities. They are the foundation for all your decisions and the source of strength when things get difficult. But you must take the time to look deep inside yourself. When you stay loyal to your beliefs, you will come out of any situation with a new understanding of yourself and the world around you."

"Loyal to myself," Vincent repeated. *So many of his previous guides had suggested the same thing, but how could he know his true self?*

"Ultimately, you have to trust in yourself and follow your heart," Ethaniel replied to Vincent's unspoken question. "This will be easier once you learn to express your emotions in healthy ways, even when it's difficult to share your feelings with others. Never suppress your honest emotions," he warned. "They are an integral part of who you are and will guide you to a place of peace and tranquility if you allow them."

Ethaniel continued to share his wisdom with Vincent as they casually strolled through the temple. "It's important to recognize and accept that no one is perfect. Everyone has flaws, faults, and imperfections. When we can embrace ours, we become more authentic. The power comes from within. Only when you can recognize and acknowledge your weaknesses can you begin to use them as strengths." He stopped for a moment and looked pointedly at Vincent. "You must accept that you are not perfect, for none of us are. We can strive for perfection, but ultimately, we must embrace that we are human and our imperfections make us unique."

Vincent nodded at Ethaniel but remained quiet.

"So, acknowledge your mistakes, learn from them, and make peace with them." Ethaniel smiled warmly at Vincent.

"You have the strength to keep going forward despite your flaws."

Despite being taken aback by Ethaniel's statement, Vincent's curiosity was further piqued. "What does it mean to take ownership of my life and choices?"

The old monk's eyes suddenly turned serious, and he continued sharing his wisdom. "The last step in finding true authenticity is accepting responsibility for your decisions," said Ethaniel. "It means understanding that every choice you make has consequences and every action brings about its results. It means being brave enough to take control of your life and acknowledge that even when things don't go as planned or expected, it's still up to you to choose how you respond. Only then will you find true freedom in life."

"You make it sound easy," Vincent said as the two continued their slow pace through the temple.

Ethaniel softly chuckled. "Taking ownership of your life and choices is not an easy task. It requires much introspection, honesty with yourself, and the willingness to confront the difficult parts of yourself that are easier to ignore. It takes courage."

Vincent nodded, understanding the lesson. "I need to embrace my flaws and imperfections to become my most authentic self."

"Yes," Ethaniel said with a smile. "Don't be fooled into thinking this is easy, though. It takes courage to face yourself without fear or judgment, make decisions even when they seem difficult, and live your life according to *your* values, not those of others."

Vincent nodded thoughtfully. Taking a deep breath, he silently made up his mind to take ownership of his life and all of its consequences. It was a daunting yet empowering decision, and he knew it was right.

"Time passes quickly," Ethaniel said gently. "It is easy to let your life slip away without noticing until suddenly you find yourself at a crossroads. Only by taking full responsibility for your life can you find true authenticity. This is the last step in the journey."

Humbled by the experience, Vincent realized he had learned more in those few moments with Ethaniel than he could ever have accomplished through years of study. A sense of peace washed over him, and his heart filled with hope.

"Walk away as quickly as you came," Ethaniel said and then parted ways with Vincent.

And as Vincent watched, Ethaniel slowly disappeared from view like a ghost in the night. The moonlight illuminated his silhouette one last time before the darkness swallowed him, and he vanished into obscurity.

There was a profound understanding within Vincent that he'd been sent to this land by an unknown force with a mysterious mission he couldn't discern. Yet, as he turned back toward his casita, his heart filled with hope, and he felt deep gratitude for the wise old monk and knew the experience would remain with him for the rest of his life.

Chapter Twelve

Whatever you do, work at it with all your heart…

—Colossians 3:23

Vincent strolled back to the comfort of the casita, feeling there was nothing left to learn. "I wonder if I've reached the end of this adventure," he said aloud to the nearby trees and animals. As he wandered, mulling over his experiences in the strange land, the wind beckoned him with a whisper. The call sounded as if it came from a nearby mountain, but he saw no one—only felt strange energy pulling him. Vincent shook his head to clear it of this imaginary sensation, and he continued his journey home.

Unexpectedly, something glowing on the mountain caught his eye. Vincent squinted and saw a resplendent figure silhouetted against the night sky: an old woman shrouded in white robes with arms outstretched like wings. She didn't move or make any sound; she just watched him.

This wasn't the most unusual occurrence Vincent had experienced in the strange land. As he studied the distant woman, warmth radiated through him, almost like an embrace.

"Vincent." The woman's tender voice reached across the distance.

While he wasn't surprised by the strange occurrences in this mysterious land anymore, how the woman spoke his name made Vincent rub his eyes to see her clearer. When his vision refocused, he saw the woman standing before him, watching him with her knowing eyes that glowed softly from within.

"Greetings, my son. I am Mia, here to bring you a message from beyond." Her voice was gentle yet strong, as if it came from far away, echoing off distant galaxies. With a slight tilt of her head and brows furrowed, Mia continued. "You have lost sight of what it means to enjoy life. When you were young, living was not just about making money or achieving things; it was also about having fun. You used to laugh and play, yet now, the responsibilities of adulthood have weighted you down so much that you have forgotten how to be joyful."

Vincent frowned. Joy had been missing from his life. Even as a child, he had focused on making money and achieving things, including his father's approval. Then came marriage and his daughters, which was joyous, but it was difficult to hold onto that feeling with his drive to achieve. He felt his heart racing and began breathing shallowly.

"I understand that life can feel overwhelming at times," Mia said, interrupting Vincent's thoughts. "But remember this: happiness is always within reach if you are willing to take time out of your busy schedule to appreciate the little moments."

"'Life will give you whatever experience is most helpful for the evolution of your consciousness[1],'" Vincent said, recalling an Eckhart Tolle quote. "Life should be a journey, not a punishment."

Mia smiled at Vincent. "Yes," she said. "It is important to enjoy life and find joy in the small things. As difficult as that may feel now, trust that happiness is waiting for you if you are willing to open your heart and welcome it in."

How simple it sounded when Mia said it, but Vincent knew it wasn't that easy. He didn't feel he was closed off to happiness, but when he considered the last time he had been joyful . . . . Well, maybe he had shut his heart down.

"Remember what it was like, Vincent," Mia said compassionately. "Remember the wonder of discovering new things and exploring the simple joys in life. You can always cherish those memories no matter how old you are." In a softer, more solemn voice, she added, "The world doesn't have to be so complicated or overwhelming. It is still possible to find happiness in the small things. Don't forget that."

Vincent's mind raced with potential opportunities for joy in his life. Again, he thought about moments with his wife and daughters, their vacations together, the silly chats they had around the table. Joy was there; he just needed to appreciate it.

"Do you remember when the simple things in life were fun?" Mia asked.

---

[1]   Eckhart Tolle, "A Quote from a New Earth," Goodreads, accessed January 22, 2023, https://www.goodreads.com/quotes/282 76-life-will-give-you-whatever-experience-is-most-helpful-for.

Vincent thought back to growing up in Sicily. He and his sisters shared so many happy times. The sensation felt foreign to him, though, as if he'd forgotten how to be care-free and adventurous. With Mia's prodding, those memories started to return. "I remember laughing and running around with my sisters," he said dreamily. "And spending time with my brother and his friends."

"The wind embraced you, and the sun shone only for you, didn't it?" Mia asked.

"Life seemed so full of possibilities then," Vincent said with a sigh.

"And why not now?" Mia prodded but didn't wait for a reply. "That is the joy of your inner child. If you embrace and nurture it, it can help you find happiness even in the darkest times."

Vincent nodded but remained silent, contemplating how to tap into the joy of his inner child. Despite trying to grasp onto his happy childhood memories, the pressures of his adult life tightened around his throat, threatening to choke him.

Mia patiently watched as Vincent struggled to embrace his inner self. Finally, she spoke softly to him. "It's difficult to find joy in life when so many worries weigh you down. But it is possible. You can't forget the simpler times when laughter was your only worry and your dreams seemed infinite. Those were the times when life was truly beautiful. So, take time to remember those days, young one."

The stars shifted in the night sky above Vincent as he focused on the joys of his youth. He remembered that though his family struggled, happiness was abundant in his early life.

Mia gave Vincent time to think about what she had said before expanding the lesson. "Finding joy isn't only about connecting with your inner child. It's also important to spend time with your friends. If you choose them correctly, they will lift your spirits and bring positive energy into your life. And this will bring you peace even in chaotic times."

"I have great friends, but we don't always have the freedom to spend quality time together," Vincent admitted.

Mia acknowledged Vincent's remark but continued giving advice. "It's important to be mindful of who you spend time with but also how you speak and respond to difficult situations."

"I often speak harshly to others when I'm overwhelmed," Vincent said remorsefully.

"It's important to step back from negative emotions and focus on what makes you happy and grateful," Mia explained. "It may be difficult at times, but it will help you make better decisions for yourself and those around you."

"Like the Eckert Tolle quote, 'If you get the inside right, the outside will fall into place[2],'" Vincent interjected. "So, in difficult times, I need to focus on the good in my life?"

Mia smiled approvingly. "Yes. The more you praise and celebrate your life, the more there is in life to celebrate."

The strangling sensation from earlier eased, and Vincent smiled. Mia's advice was empowering and something he could apply to improve his life—and the lives of the people around him.

"Happiness can be found in your daily routines, too," Mia continued.

---

[2] Ami Kulkarni, "'If You Get the inside Right, the Outside Will Fall into Place' - Eckhart Tolle," Arkadiance, April 27, 2017, https://arkadiance.com/blogs/the-elegant-forager/if-you-get-the-inside-right-the-outside-will-fall-into-place-eckhart-tolle#:~:text=%22%20%2D%20Eckh%20%E2%80%93%20Arkadiance-,%22If%20you%20get%20the%20inside%20right%2C%20the%20outside%20will,fall%20into%20place%22%20%2D%20Eckhart%

"Even in the mundane tasks?" Vincent asked.

After Mia nodded, Vincent looked inward to uncover what made him happy. Soon, he realized that the small things he'd taken for granted brought him the most joy: a beautiful sunrise, the laughter of children, the smell of freshly-brewed coffee .... All these things could bring him joy if he chose to notice them.

"Remember," Mia said, "you don't have to wait for extraordinary circumstances to experience joy. It's always present. Just open your eyes, look within, and choose to embrace the beauty in each moment. This is where happiness lies." After a short pause, she added, "It all starts with being open to new experiences, letting go of preconceived notions, and learning something new. Step outside your comfort zone and explore the possibilities that await. Embrace your imagination and enjoy your journey."

"The journey is just as important as reaching the destination," Vincent said, tapping into the wise woman's knowledge. He was beginning to understand this sage's lesson and expected Mia to take her leave.

Instead, Mia continued to impart wisdom, expanding on the knowledge of happiness. "True happiness comes when you let go of all judgments and learn to laugh at yourself, especially in moments you feel embarrassed or silly." Abruptly, Mia broke out in a laugh that echoed off the mountain.

After the surprise of her action wore off, Vincent found himself unable to control his laughter and joined her. "I feel lighter already!" he exclaimed through his fit of giggles.

Mia composed herself and continued advising Vincent. "Consider, also, that seeking the approval of others is not the path to happiness."

That simple sentence brought an end to Vincent's mirth. His memories took him back to his childhood efforts to gain his father's approval. Despite the happiness he found around his mother and siblings, the emotions surrounding pleasing his father made Vincent's body tense and rigid.

"It's okay to have sought others' approval in the past, Vincent. That is done and gone," Mia said tenderly. "Happiness can only be found within yourself. It's time to release the expectations you think others have of you and simply be true to who you are."

"But—" Vincent began but was immediately cut off.

"If people don't like that you're not living to meet their expectations, that's their problem, not yours." Mia's response was stern but supportive.

Vincent exhaled a breath he didn't realize he was holding. He knew Mia was correct, but it helped him to have someone give him permission to not care about others' expectations of him. As he looked at the wise woman, she began to fade like a ghost about to depart.

"Finally," Mia said, "be prepared for the surprises in life. You can never be certain what's coming around the corner, so it's best to accept it and learn to laugh at it."

"Like a roller coaster."

"Exactly," Mia said. "Sometimes you have great highs; other times, there are scary lows. But as long as you're ready for whatever comes your way, you will enjoy the ride." She winked at him with a bright smile that soon faded.

Now, Vincent was certain their time together was coming to an end.

"Time passes quickly, and life can be short. Promise me and yourself that you will take the opportunity to enjoy it," Mia said.

"I promise I will," Vincent said with a sad smile. Final moments before parting were difficult. He recalled the death of his father, who had fallen and hit his head. For days, his father didn't wake up, and the test results confirmed that he was in an irreversible coma.

The family's decision to remove Vincent's father from life support was agonizing but the right thing to do. As they gathered around him, heartbreak permeated the hospital room. Time seemed to stop as everyone said their goodbyes. They kept vigil with tear-filled eyes and listened as the machines beeped slowly and then slower, each beep signifying a step closer to their final farewell. Collectively, they hoped for a miracle, but Vincent knew what was coming.

Finally, the mechanical noise representing his father's life fell silent and was replaced by the sorrowful sounds of a family accepting death's harsh reality. But in that moment of grieving together, Vincent realized how much his father meant to him and everyone in the room. That moment was forever imprinted in his mind.

Vincent's sad smile transformed into a frown as he remembered his father. Despite all their difficulties while growing up, he had come to appreciate his father as he raised his own children. In fact, he had grown very close to his father.

Years after moving to America, Vincent's father began sharing stories about his life growing up. Somehow, these accounts of his father's childhood created a bridge between them, a bond that strengthened over the years. Vincent began to understand that his father had done his best to provide for his family.

"Life is fragile and fleeting." Mia narrowed her eyes at Vincent. "So, enjoy every moment," she warned.

Mia's advice shifted Vincent's melancholy to an unexpected surge of enthusiasm. He was excited to explore new places, take risks, and try new activities despite fear or apprehension and was determined to live each moment like it was his last.

Mia's image had nearly disappeared when her voice echoed in the air once more. "Life is beautiful. Go forward and make the most of it, Vincent."

Even though the wise woman had gone, her words lingered within Vincent's heart. Humbled and grateful, he fell to his knees. With a bowed head and clasped hands, Vincent prayed, "Thank you for the gift of Mia. Life is indeed beautiful. Please let me hold her lessons in my heart as I continue forward."

Chapter Thirteen

In everything I did, I showed you that by this kind
of hard work we must help the weak, remembering the words
the Lord Jesus himself said: "It is more blessed
to give than to receive."

—Acts 20:35

V incent spent much of the following day walking through
the jungle. Occasionally, he would stop and sit with his
back to a tree, thinking about all the lessons he had
learned so far. He desired to get back to his life and put into
practice what he'd learned, but he was still apprehensive.
*What if there's more I need to know? What if I get caught up
in the mundane and forget this place?* No, he wasn't ready
to return. There was still more to see and learn in this
mysterious place. He was sure of it.

The sun slowly set along the horizon, and night descended upon the forest's verdant foliage, bringing an end to Vincent's self-reflective day. The warm summer air was filled with a chorus of chirping crickets and singing birds, providing the perfect accompaniment to a peaceful evening.

But then, a stranger appeared. He greeted Vincent with a friendly smile and said, "My friend, you have been here a while. Soon, you will have to make some decisions."

"I know," Vincent admitted. "I have been reflecting on this all day. I'm . . . I don't think I'm ready to decide." He couldn't help but notice the stranger's many tattoos, which seemed to represent a long journey for wisdom and strength. The man radiated a powerful and intellectual aura that drew Vincent in.

"Walk with me," the stranger said, motioning for Vincent to follow. "I'm Newo," he began as Vincent joined him. "I have been learning about and from many different cultures for centuries."

Without hesitation, Vincent took pace beside Newo, eager to tap into the knowledge of the powerful shaman. As they walked out of the trees and into the sunlight, he noticed that Newo's robes shimmered as if imbued with magic.

The man retrieved a small wooden talisman from his robe of animal hides and caressed the carvings with his thumb as they walked. "Before we begin, I think it's important that you know who I am. In my years, I have seen and done many things." Newo's eyes focused on the distance like he saw his past play before him as he spoke. "I've been a warrior, fighting many enemies and surviving battles no one thought possible. I am a healer, harnessing natural energies to help people improve physically and spiritually. But above all, I stand for justice and will always stand with those in need and help them push forward."

Vincent didn't know where this conversation with Newo was going, but he remained silently walking beside his companion.

"Charity isn't confined to giving money or goods. It includes showing others how much they matter by being present and attentive. It's a way of sharing kindness and compassion with others." Newo's gaze returned to the present. "You have a lot of influence in your life, Vincent. It's time to use your abundance to help others."

Newo continued to speak about his own life experiences, illustrating what it meant to live abundantly through generous actions. He spoke of the joys and blessings that come to those willing to give freely, using examples from his background that emphasized the importance of charity as one way of cultivating respect for all people and promoting peace among them.

"Generosity," Newo said, "is giving with an open heart without expecting anything in return. These can be large or small gestures, but it is essential to show kindness toward others." After a few steps in silence, he continued. "Charity is being generous even when it comes at a personal cost or sacrifice. What are some ways you can help people around you who are less fortunate, even if it requires you to step back from your own goals momentarily?"

Pondering Newo's words, Vincent was reminded that Jesus often spoke of abundance and giving to the less fortunate. *Give, and it will be given to you. Good measure, pressed down, shaken together, and running over, will be poured into your lap. For with the measure you use, it will be measured to you* (Luke 6:38).

"The Golden Rule," Vincent said and took a deep breath. "Aside from donating money or supplies to causes, I can volunteer at local charities and schools and be more available for my family and friends when they need help."

Newo looked over at Vincent and smiled. "Those are wonderful ideas," he said. "You may be surprised when I say this, but you must focus on yourself before giving to others. I know you have struggled with this, Vincent, but you must not forget to love and nurture yourself too. This self-care and self-love will serve as the foundation for you to give generously from a place of joy and abundance."

"So," Vincent began, "generosity isn't only about giving what I can, but also allowing me to receive and appreciate whatever gifts the Universe brings, embracing this exchange with gratitude?"

"You are a fast learner," Newo commented. "You must give to receive. If you take all for yourself and never give to others, then soon enough, you will find there is nothing left to take. But if you open your heart and are willing to share what you have with others, then something truly magical can happen. A beautiful exchange occurs when you have the right mindset and are willing to give freely without expectations. Your giving will come back to you through material items or intangible gifts like good luck, clarity of vision, and joy."

"I must give in order to receive," Vincent repeated.

"Something that will help further is accepting that, even though you may feel isolated and alone at times, all humans are connected—to each other and the Universe." Newo motioned to the sky. "We are made up of stardust—literally. Our atoms were created in the fiery cores of stars long before being dispersed into space through supernovas. Each cell in our bodies is composed of these same elements."

"That means we contain galaxies within us," Vincent said with a chuckle.

Newo smirked at Vincent's observation before continuing. "Humans continually interact with the Universe, whether breathing the air or eating food. The oxygen in each breath flows from the broken-down molecules from plants that use photosynthesis to take light energy from the sun.

"Beyond physical connections," Newo went on, "humans have a spiritual bond with the Universe too. For millennia, people have gazed at the stars and planets in the night skies to try to make sense of their lives and experiences. People find solace in knowing they play an integral role in a much larger picture and can connect with it."

"It's hard to wrap my brain around something so expansive," Vincent admitted, "but I know this concept will provide peace and understanding. No matter how insignificant or small life feels, all of us are connected to something much larger than ourselves." Vincent felt humbled as he spoke these enlightened words.

His revelation pleased Newo. "God has a plan for all of us. It is our job to discover it. He wants to give us more things in life than we can imagine."

The two walked through the jungle together, with a comfortable silence hanging between them. Vincent allowed Newo's lessons to sink in and looked for ways to apply them to his life.

After passing a clearing in the jungle, Newo spoke again. "God gives us gifts in the form of love, beauty, peace, and joy. He gives us strength and courage when we are faced with difficulties. He also provides opportunities for personal growth and transformation, usually when we least expect them."

Vincent nodded. "Our lives become enriched as we open ourselves to receive God's blessings."

"You need to take the time to reflect on your life and goals. Only then will you recognize what God is offering," Newo advised.

Vincent pondered the knowledge he had gained in this mystical land and how it could bring great fortune if followed. In speaking with Newo, he became aware that the greatest treasures of wealth, happiness, and joy are not found through objects or money but are already within. If Vincent put this wisdom into practice, the rewards would be plentiful.

No longer would he need to search for approval from others or yearn for material items. Instead, Vincent could find fulfillment simply by doing what was right and embracing his inner potential. Through his newfound awareness, Vincent felt confident exploring the world of possibilities. He was ready to let go of the past and look forward, embracing all that life had to offer.

"I have learned so much," Vincent said as their walk slowed to a saunter. "In processing what you've shared with me, I understand more what God is offering me: job security, financial stability, traveling, and I know with work, meaningful relationships with loved ones. I know there is so much more, but I need to take time to recognize and appreciate it."

"We each have the potential to create something beautiful in this life. With the right mindset and the willingness to give freely without expectation, an astonishing exchange takes place. When you give love, blessings will shower down upon you like rain," Newo said, and almost instantly, raindrops fell upon them as the path took them to the edge of the tree line.

The gentle rain was comforting. Vincent held out his hands and looked up, unable to stop himself from laughing.

Newo had released something in him that had been holding him back. But when Vincent returned his attention to his walking companion, the space beside him was empty.

As Vincent lowered his arms, he noticed a small capsule—a talisman—resting on the palm of each of his hands. He knew these contained a specific knowledge or truth that would help him on his journey.

Overwhelmed with gratitude for Newo's kindness, Vincent turned around to walk back to his casita. "Thank you," he said to the shaman.

Chapter Fourteen

For you have been born again, not of perishable seed,
but of imperishable, through the living and
enduring word of God.

—1 Peter 1:23

A fire's warm glow caught Vincent's attention. The sun
had peeked through the clouds just before dusk, and
the air smelled fresh. Having always been fascinated
by flames, Vincent strolled toward the fire. A strange calm
washed over him as he approached.

The firelight brought into focus the encampment's
details. In contrast to the darkness creeping in around it,
everything near the flames appeared sharper and more
vivid. Several concrete benches surrounded the glow, each
one slightly different from the others.

Vincent sat on the one that called out to him—not knowing why he picked the one he did—and quietly watched the embers dancing in the flames. His eyes followed the mesmerizing patterns of the orange and yellow flickering light, which relaxed his mind and body. The distinct and pleasant aroma of burning pine filled his nostrils as the sound of the crackling wood echoed off nearby trees.

As he watched, Vincent's thoughts wandered back to his childhood, to the times he often found himself fixated on open fires—looking for shapes or faces within them or imagining stories about what caused them to burn so brightly. The powerful flames captivated him; he wondered how they could turn something that was once cold and still into something alive, energetic, beautiful, and ever-changing right before his eyes.

The heat radiating off the fire was warm but not too intense—just enough to be comfortable. Vincent reached out with his arm to feel its gentle warmth against his skin. Eventually, he reached for some nearby twigs, which he fed, piece by piece, into the fire's hungry mouth, creating new bright yellow tendrils that spread quickly like tiny stars across its surface before eventually fading completely into nothingness again.

While gazing into the fire, Vincent saw a figure approaching out of the corner of his eye, and he turned to see who it was. He struggled to make out the details, but he could only tell the person was young. Despite the darkness, the individual glowed. The figure had long hair—possibly brown—that framed the face and rested limply on their shoulders.

As the individual neared, Vincent discerned a thin but muscular build, suggesting strength and endurance beyond what one would expect from someone young. Still, he couldn't figure out whether his visitor was male or female.

"Welcome, friend," the person said with a voice like velvet.

Instantly, Vincent knew the person wasn't completely human. He could feel an aura of magic as the individual neared. After a few more steps, he was finally able to see the person clearly. Vincent detected an ancientness about the man, yet the stranger looked to be no more than twenty-five.

The man's brown hair framed dark eyes and high cheekbones. His clothes were loose, lightweight, earthly-colored—browns and greens—garments that moved perfectly with his body as he approached.

Could he have been watching me all afternoon? Vincent wondered, realizing the stranger blended into the surrounding scenery, almost like he was a part of it. The thought was both startling and comforting when Vincent noticed the quiver of arrows on his back and the exquisite bow in his hand, crafted from wood so twisted it seemed alive.

"Who are you? Where did you come from?" Vincent asked after the stranger declined to say anything more after the greeting.

The silence lingered as the man briefly made eye contact with Vincent, then returned to gazing at the landscape. Vincent wasn't sure if the stranger heard him or understood English.

When Vincent opened his mouth to ask again in Italian, the man said, "I am Cristian. I'm from everywhere and nowhere."

As cryptic as the response was, Vincent somehow felt relieved, as though hearing Cristian's words had lifted a weight off him. He gestured for Cristian to join him on the bench, and the two stared into the fire together.

Without speaking aloud, Cristian spoke to Vincent's mind, sharing (and showing) stories of his adventures in otherworldly places. What stood out most to Vincent about the tales was the recurring theme that, despite the odds being stacked against Cristian, he always remained true to himself—fearless and powerful but also gentle.

"It's most important," Cristian finally said aloud, "that you do not fear death. You see, fear stops you from living the life intended for you."

Immediately, Vincent cringed and thought about his father's passing. But he didn't have much time to venture down that road before Cristian spoke again.

"Would you like to hear a story?" he asked.

"Are you going to show me this one in my mind?" Vincent asked.

Cristian smiled and shook his head. "This one, I will speak. It's a parable of two men: one who lived in fear and one who embraced his mortality," he began. "Both men were gifted with the same life-changing opportunities to find true happiness. What neither of the men knew was that it was the way they chose to live that determined their paths.

"The first man was terrified of death and its consequences. He believed he could protect himself if he feared death. So, he locked himself away and refused to take risks or explore new opportunities. In his mind, any potential danger or risk was too great compared to the security he had created by avoiding them.

"The second man saw his mortality differently. Convinced that if he wanted to live a life free from fear and anxiety, he had to make peace with death. So, he accepted and embraced his mortality rather than run from it. He understood that it is by embracing death that we can fully appreciate the life we have on Earth.

"Which man do you think found true happiness?" Cristian asked.

The answer seemed easy to Vincent. "The second."

Cristian nodded. "While the first man remained *safe*, the second explored everything life had to offer. He was able to seize every moment with passion and enthusiasm as if it were his last, like traveling to new places to learn about the people of different cultures and the knowledge they held. Yet, he still allowed himself time to relax in nature whenever he felt overwhelmed."

Vincent was captivated by Cristian's story but couldn't understand how accepting death could be beneficial. The idea of being free from all fears intrigued him, though.

As if reading Vincent's thoughts, Cristian said, "By accepting your mortality, you can liberate yourself from anxiety. Fear will no longer shackle you; instead, you can open yourself up with trust and curiosity without worrying about what might happen.

"Additionally, by learning to accept death, you come closer to understanding why life exists, appreciating its fragility yet savoring each moment with deep gratitude. Free yourself from all fears, including those associated with death, and you can explore all the possibilities available during your brief passage on Earth, unburdened and untethered by any preoccupation or limitation created by self-doubt or apprehension."

Although Vincent wanted to embrace Cristian's message, doubts still clouded his mind. "It sounds like a fairy tale," he said skeptically. "How can you possibly face death and still live?"

Cristian smiled knowingly and responded, "It is not make-believe; it's very real. To understand it, we must go back to the beginning of time, to the moment the Universe was created. It is at this moment that we find an answer to your question.

"When the Universe was first formed, two forces were present: Life and Death. They were opposites yet equally powerful, and both had their place in our world. At first, they coexisted harmoniously, but one day, something changed, and Life began to gain power over Death.

"This newfound power meant that Life could create more living things faster than Death could destroy them, thus establishing an ever-growing population of living beings in the Universe. It also meant that the balance between Life and Death shifted, with Life becoming stronger than Death and coming out victorious in whatever battles they fought against each other.

"But no matter how powerful Life became, it never fully won against Death. You see, even though Death may have been pushed away from some places, it never really disappeared because it was always lurking just beneath the surface, waiting for its chance to regain its strength and reclaim its rightful place alongside Life.

"What does this have anything to do with facing death head-on? Well, it's because of this eternal struggle between Life and Death that humans have always been close to both forces. We have seen firsthand how powerful each can be—so much so that most people choose not to risk their lives by getting too close to death. Instead, people tend to choose to live far away from either one of them, where they are safe from any danger.

"But what if someone wanted to get closer? What if someone wanted to experience both forces at full strength without fear? That is when facing death head-on comes into play. It's when someone chooses not only to get close but also takes control of their destiny by deliberately putting themselves into dangerous situations to experience the full force of Life and Death simultaneously."

Vincent rubbed his temple as he tried to wrap his mind around this idea.

But Cristian wasn't done explaining. "I know this is a lot," he said, "but let me continue. When someone takes a stand against Death by actively seeking out danger instead of running away from it, then surpassing Death means being reborn into a new kind of Life—one which has faced its greatest enemy and came out unscathed as a victor instead of a victim; as the master rather than a slave; as conqueror not conquered.

"In other words, anyone who has faced Death head-on will find themselves changed in ways beyond imagining. They will suddenly be free from worry or fear about dying since nothing can hurt them anymore. And this newfound freedom brings unimaginable opportunities for real fulfillment like never before. It is no wonder why so many great heroes throughout history chose this path over all else. After all, what greater achievement is there than subduing Death itself?"

Vincent shrugged, still apprehensive about what facing death meant for him.

"You have nothing to fear," Cristian reassured him. "Let me tell you what God has said about death."

Upon hearing this, Vincent's brow raised, and the doubt subsided.

"God's words about death are quite clear," Cristian began. "He tells us that we shouldn't be afraid of death 'for the living know that they will die, but the dead know nothing' (Ecclesiastes 9:5). He also assures us that those who have died will find comfort and peace in Heaven, where they await their return to Earth."

Vincent nodded. He knew the verse Cristian quoted but had never taken the time to internalize its meaning.

Cristian placed a reassuring hand on Vincent's shoulder. "The Almighty has promised you eternal life if you remain true in your faith and follow his commandments. He is our protector and provider and will never forsake us, even after death. Heaven is a place of joy and peace, where those who have lived righteously may forever reside with him in perfect harmony."

Emotion overwhelmed Vincent as he listened to Cristian's words of assurance. Tears welled in his eyes. "God loves us and wants what is best for everyone in every way possible," he said with awe.

With a smile, Cristian created a vision of Heaven in Vincent's mind. "What awaits you is unparalleled serenity among lush meadows filled with fragrant flowers. All varieties of fruit trees line peaceful rivers. Majestic snow-capped mountain border celestial cities wrapped in white marble walls that stretch from horizon to horizon. And all of this is blanketed by an aura of love emanating from the Father, enveloping everyone who enters Heaven's gates."

As Vincent experienced Cristian's vision, he felt the peace of God entering his heart and breathed a sigh of relief.

"Awards are waiting there, too," Cristian said as he ended the visual story in Vincent's mind. "There is forgiveness of sins, new opportunities for spiritual and intellectual growth, and the fellowship of other believers. Most importantly," he said with a smile, "you have the opportunity to spend eternity worshiping God."

After the visions and promises that Cristian offered, Vincent knew without a doubt that it was possible for anyone, regardless of their sins and mistakes, to gain admission into Heaven. But he understood that people had to turn away from sin for their spirit to be welcomed home by God.

Knowing this gave Vincent hope and assurance in this strange new land full of unexplored mysteries, both delightful and terrifying. He no longer feared death but eagerly awaited what lay ahead in this beautiful world full of excitement and joys unknown yet sure to come, all thanks to God's loving arms, always ready to embrace him even here so far from home.

The air was still, and the fire burnt brightly. Flames seemed to lap hungrily at the night sky; their energy and vigor were apparent to all who observed. Vincent watched, mesmerized, as Cristian rose from the bench and stood before the blaze, motionless and transfixed.

Time stood still as Cristian remained in that spot, with his back turned towards Vincent. But then, gradually, something began to change. It started with a subtle glow emanating from Cristian's body. The light grew stronger with each passing second until it expanded into a brilliant halo of white around him.

As Vincent looked on in amazement, the halo burst into a column of pure energy that shot up toward the heavens above them. The column quickly shifted shape and color until it resembled an enormous phoenix soaring ever higher, its wings outstretched as if to embrace the Universe itself.

At that moment, Vincent understood what was happening: Cristian had found a way to transcend death without fear or hesitation—he had become one with the eternal fire of life itself. He watched in awe as the phoenix eventually disappeared, leaving an empty space where Cristian had once stood. Vincent contemplated a pile of ashes smoldering on the ground, which was all that remained of Christian's physical form after his soul had been set free to explore endless possibilities beyond this world.

Vincent stood silently for many minutes afterward before finally finding words to express himself. "That . . . was incredible!" he said breathlessly. "I've seen some amazing things in my life, but nothing quite like this."

He couldn't help but feel humbled by what he'd just witnessed; Cristian's courage and strength displayed so poetically at such a crucial juncture in life deeply inspired Vincent. If someone as wise and experienced as Cristian could find peace and acceptance after facing death, surely he could too? He certainly hoped so.

With one final glance at the pile of ashes, Vincent slowly turned away from the fading fire and resumed his journey through the jungle, comforted by the knowledge that mortality didn't necessarily have to mean finality.

Maybe there was more than one ending for our lives—unexpected ones, too—if we were brave enough to take chances and make sacrifices when necessary.

Chapter Fifteen

Above all, love each other deeply,
because love covers over a multitude of sins.

—1 Peter 4:8

Vincent felt like he had been in this strange land for weeks now, and he was beginning to feel overwhelmed by the sheer number of magical and mystical moments he had been thrown into. While each one offered him a glimpse into something special and unique, it was also hard not to be tired from all the different experiences that he had encountered.

But as he journeyed the following day, Vincent found himself at a place unlike any other. It was impossibly beautiful: lush green fields and rolling hills stretched to the horizon. The sun shone brightly on this place—more brilliantly than anywhere else—causing everything to look warm and inviting. And in the middle stood an old oak tree, tall and proud, like an ancient guardian watching over this special place.

It was beneath this tree that Vincent noticed something else: a woman with long, silver hair sitting quietly, looking up at the rising sun with an expression of awe on her face. She seemed so completely out of place that he couldn't resist the urge to be closer to her.

When Vincent stopped in front of her, she greeted him warmly. "Welcome, Vincent. I am Caterina." The cadence of her words was slow and gentle, brimming with love. She studied him for a moment, then said, "I have lived a long, full life and have seen much joy and sorrow throughout the years. I am here to tell you that life is much simpler if you can love everyone and everything."

Vincent looked into the old woman's eyes and felt an understanding between them. It was as though she had already passed on some of her knowledge to him just through their exchange of glances. He nodded in agreement, and a strange calm washed over him.

Caterina continued speaking with a whimsical tone as if she were telling a fairytale. "My dear boy," she said affectionately, "if you decide to open your heart to the world and embrace its beauty without judgment or expectation, then you will find that miracles can occur for you each and every day. This is what it means to love all around you."

There was a small pause as Caterina took a deep breath and smiled at her surroundings. "It does not mean that every-thing will always be perfect, but it does mean that there is hope for great things to come if we trust in the power of love."

These words enraptured Vincent; they gave him hope that his journey would eventually lead somewhere beautiful and fulfilling. "Could you give me more details about what it means to love everything?"

Instead of giving a direct answer, Caterina smiled knowingly and began telling a story from long ago...

"Once upon a time, there lived a great sage named Tatiana, who had dedicated her life to understanding love on the deepest level possible. One day, Tatiana set out on a magical quest to uncover the source of love's power—but much to her surprise, she found nothing at all—nothing except a void.

"At first, Tatiana was confused and disheartened. She returned from her journey and pondered the meaning for days. Finally, one day she realized the answer she'd been looking for: Love was everywhere! It was in the twinkle of stars on a clear night sky, in the smile of a stranger passing by, and even in our struggles and hardships. At that moment, Tatiana knew that true love goes beyond anything we can see or touch—an ever-present force that binds us all together regardless of circumstance or situation."

Vincent wanted to feel hope from Caterina's story, but he couldn't grasp how to transform the void he felt into love.

Caterina nodded, somehow knowing Vincent was struggling. "Tatiana's revelation came full circle when she realized that if we truly want to simplify our lives, we should start by loving ourselves. Only then can we open our hearts enough to fully embrace those around us as well as the world at large.

"You must understand, young one, loving yourself first is indeed the hardest thing you will ever do. It requires bravery and courage, dedication and commitment. You must take ownership of your own life and accept responsibility—for your successes and failures. That is when you can truly begin to love yourself without reservation or hesitation."

Vincent sat beside Caterina, silently digesting everything she had said. He had thought about loving himself before, but it still seemed selfish and vanity driven. But something told him that the old woman understood what she was talking about, and he shifted to intently listening as she continued speaking.

"It is only when you love yourself that you can truly give love to others," Caterina said softly. "When you can look into the mirror each morning without guilt or shame but with acceptance and understanding, then you have begun to walk the path to self-love." She took a cleansing breath and said, "It can be hard at times because of all the expectations placed upon us by society, but if we can remember that we are more than our physical appearance or social status, then we can start to appreciate ourselves for who we are on the inside."

"So, I need to love myself first to love others?" Vincent asked.

"Yes. I know it sounds cliché, but it really is true. It takes a great deal of inner strength to look past all of our perceived flaws and instead embrace them as part of who we are," Caterina explained. "But once we do this, amazing things happen around us. Doors open, which lead us down roads that bring out our best selves."

"It does sound cliché," Vincent admitted with a chuckle.

Caterina looked at Vincent with kind eyes before speaking again: "Remember, my young friend, there may be days when loving yourself seems impossible. Sometimes it will feel like no matter how hard you try, nothing seems to work. But don't give up. We all have days like this, and it's important not to let them discourage us from continuing on our paths toward self-love." She paused for a moment before adding, "Just remember that no one else can complete this journey for you. Take each day slowly, move through it one step at a time, and eventually, love will become easier than hate."

"Some people are too hard to love, though," Vincent admitted.

"My dear," Caterina said, "loving people who are difficult is part of the journey. Do you recall what Jesus taught about this?"

Vincent had a vague idea of the scripture Caterina alluded to but invited her to tell him more.

A tea set appeared beside Caterina. Without blinking an eye at the impossibility of that, she poured two cups and offered one to Vincent. "Jesus taught us that we must love those who are difficult to love because it reflects God's love for us. He understands how hard it can be to extend patience and kindness to those who don't seem to deserve it. But this act reflects God's own infinite mercy and willingness to forgive us no matter how much we have wronged him."

Caterina took another sip of her tea before continuing with her explanation. "Jesus showed us the importance of loving everyone— even those who are hard to love—by setting an example through his own life and death on the cross. He was willing to forgive all sorts of people no matter how great their sins were against him or others."

Vincent nodded in agreement as he took in what she was saying. His thoughts reminded him of many situations when Jesus forgave those who wronged him.

"The Bible tells us, 'For if you forgive other people when they sin against you, your heavenly Father will also forgive you' (Matthew 6:14). You must learn to forgive those who have wronged you just like Jesus did for us—even if it may be difficult at times."

"It can be *very* difficult at times," Vincent admitted.

Caterina rested her hand on Vincent's and looked deep into his eyes, speaking with passion and conviction. "We must remember that God loves all people—no matter how broken or sinful they may be. We must learn from Jesus's example and extend grace and mercy toward others just like he did for us.

"As followers of God, we should strive to follow Jesus's teachings by showing unconditional love towards others even when it gets tough or uncomfortable. It is only through this kind of love that real change can take place in our lives."

"It looks like I have a choice to make," Vincent admitted, although it wasn't the choice he felt he had to make the day before.

"You do," Caterina agreed with a smile. "Will you choose love or emptiness? If you choose to love everyone and everything around you, life is full of joy, beauty, and meaning—even if it's difficult at times. But if you choose to turn away from his people and the world around you, there won't be much in life with real value. It will be cold and lonely without love. So ask yourself: Which path will bring me true happiness? The choice is yours."

Vincent felt himself at a crossroads. He consciously had to decide whether he would live with love for everything and everyone or with a lack of love, holding onto the belief that life is meaningless.

"The choice may seem impossible," Caterina said, cutting into his thoughts, "but trust me when I say living with love is the only way for you to find true happiness and fulfillment. If you choose to show love everywhere and embrace all the people around you, you will have joy and meaning in your life.

"But if instead of choosing love, you shield yourself from that emotion and allow negative thoughts and feelings to dictate your days, then I'm afraid those days will be empty." Caterina looked at Vincent sadly. "If you can decide to love everything now, you will set yourself up for a life filled with meaning and joy."

Vincent tried to comprehend the gravity of her words and their implications for his life.

Caterina smiled at Vincent in a way that was both knowing and loving. "I have seen too many people try to change the world around them without ever understanding that one cannot change another person's heart. We may think we're playing a part in helping others, but ultimately, they must decide who they want to be on their own," she said. "The only thing anyone can do is love and accept those around them as they are."

Vincent thought back to the moments when he had tried to persuade others to act differently or take a certain stance. He realized with shame how his attempts had been futile; all he had achieved was frustration and disappointment, both for himself and for those he wanted to help.

He bowed his head in shame as Caterina continued speaking, her voice soft yet firm. "Love is powerful because it doesn't require us to do anything more than just love who they are and what they do, no matter how different it may be from our own beliefs or values."

She placed a comforting hand on Vincent's shoulder and added, "It is not your job to judge or control anyone else—you are only responsible for loving them unconditionally. But remember, this doesn't mean enabling bad behavior or tolerating mistreatment. Love means allowing others the freedom to make their own choices while still being accepted and appreciated."

At these words, Vincent felt a strange sensation come over him. It was almost as if his entire being suddenly filled up with compassion and empathy towards himself and all those around him.

Then Vincent remembered a day when he felt shame for being so judgmental. It was a cold winter day, and his family was having dinner with some extended relatives at a restaurant. There was one particular relative that Vincent had never met before, who had just recently moved from out of town. She arrived late for dinner and had been talking about her new life in the city.

Everyone at the table seemed mesmerized by her stories—except for Vincent. Instead of focusing on her stories, he judged her based on her clothing and mannerisms. In his mind, he thought she was too flashy and ill-mannered for someone so young. Looking around the table, it was obvious the others thought she was charming and interesting; however, he still felt uneasy about her presence. As a result, Vincent remained quiet during most of the dinner and only spoke up occasionally to make passive-aggressive comments or jokes.

At the end of the night, when it was time to say goodbye, she thanked everyone for inviting her and said that it had been lovely getting to know us all better. That's when Vincent felt overwhelming guilt for being so judgmental towards her earlier in the evening.

Now, Vincent realized he had allowed his preconceived notions of what *proper* behavior should look like to cloud his opinions instead of actually getting to know this person as an individual.

Vincent blinked several times and shook his head, snapping out of the memory and the shame he felt for it. Revisiting that memory with the knowledge Caterina imparted to him sparked a feeling of wonderment, which sparkled in his eyes as he looked over at her.

"I can do this," Vincent said. "I can let go of past expectations and judgments and choose love instead of fear or judgment when faced with any situation." He knew it wouldn't be easy at times, but he also knew it would be worth it in the end—just like Caterina had promised him before starting this leg of the journey together.

"You can," Caterina agreed and placed her empty teacup on the tray.

As night fell over the forest clearing where they sat, Vincent spoke about his newfound understanding deep within himself. "My job going forward is simply to love everything and everyone, regardless of differences or disagreements."

"Embrace the peace that will come with this mindset, and it will reign over all aspects of your life. And as long as you stay true to this truth," Caterina said, "you will never again feel the weight of the world upon your shoulders." She rose to her feet and smiled down at Vincent before walking out of the clearing.

Vincent watched closely as Caterina slowly faded into the trees. A multitude of questions and emotions arose in his heart, but also an undeniable feeling of peace and serenity. He had been granted the ability to view life from a different perspective, one filled with love and acceptance of everything around him.

The sun slowly began to set, casting an orange hue on the sky as he sat alone in silence. He felt deeply connected to Caterina, his newfound awareness giving him a sense of clarity about love. Of course, he couldn't help but wonder who she really was. Would he ever cross paths with her again? Regardless, her wisdom would stay with Vincent throughout his life.

Taking a deep breath, Vincent closed his eyes for a moment before standing to embrace his journey forward. He understood now more than ever that if he wanted to change the world, he must start by loving it first.

Chapter Sixteen

You make known to me the path of life;
you will fill me with joy in your presence,
with eternal pleasures at your right hand.

—Psalm 16:11

Vincent's eyes were wide open, but he lay motionless in a trance as if some mysterious force had taken over his body, drawing him into a deep state of meditation and stillness. There was a lightness in him, like someone had erased all the worries and troubles of the world.

As he remained unable to move, Vincent realized just how powerful the experience in the mysterious land truly was—it had allowed him to tap into something far greater than himself. It was a reminder that there is something much bigger out there than what he could see or understand with physical senses alone, something cosmic and eternal that binds everyone together as one human community united by love and compassion for all life on Earth.

Suddenly, Vincent felt himself drifting upward like an invisible force was pulling him into another realm—beyond his physical body and limited comprehension. As he ascended further and further away from earthly reality, thoughts flashed through his mind like lightning bolts: memories from long ago resurfaced from deep within his subconsciousness; feelings he hadn't experienced before filled his soul; ideas and visions bubbled up within him like never before.

As he stood in a new place, Vincent looked up towards the heavens above, gazing with wonder as the stars sparkled and danced against an ethereal backdrop of galaxies upon galaxies. He felt connected to something much larger than himself for the first time, some universal truth that transcended all boundaries or limitations separating us on Earth.

Before him, a figure appeared, dressed in white robes draped across its body with long hair that cascaded down over its shoulders like a flowing river. Vincent couldn't focus on the person for too long; it was like looking through a fogged glass pane or seeing a mirage dancing in desert sands across vast distances. What he could see, however, was that its features were mostly indistinct, but its face glowed with an inner radiance.

The figure gestured toward Vincent with open arms, inviting him closer, and said, "Trust in me always. Put your heart in my hands and feel my deep love for you. Love me, and all will be revealed in time."

"Who—" Vincent began and stepped forward, but the figure faded from sight.

THE BUDDHA WHO DROVE A BENTLEY

"I have been watching you for some time. You were put on earth to do great things, but only if you follow me. I have waited for you patiently."

When Vincent looked around, nobody was there—just an empty path stretching out before him. He thought his imagination was playing tricks on him, but then, a warm sensation swept through Vincent's body.

"Listen carefully. If you follow my guidance, I promise that your life will become something far greater than what it is now—something beautiful and meaningful."

This time, Vincent froze as goosebumps rose on his skin. This could only mean one thing... the presence of God. A spiritual energy that seemed to emanate from everywhere surrounded him. And God had spoken directly to him, something he had long yearned for. He covered his face with his hands as tears started flowing.

"Why do you cry?" The words vibrated through every molecule in the air.

The voice of God, Vincent thought. At this realization, his breathing slowed and became shallow. Startled by the realness of it all, he wiped away the tears, clearing his vision. Standing before him was an angelic figure with its hands outstretched towards him as if offering comfort and guidance during this difficult time in his life.

"I . . . I do not know," Vincent admitted. He did know, though, but putting his emotions in words seemed a difficult undertaking at that moment.

Immediately, the next question was asked. "What is it that you seek?"

Feeling overwhelmed yet reassured at the same time by its presence, Vincent spoke directly to God. "I seek assurance that this path is the one you want me to take and if it was your will that guided me onto my current course of action."

God nodded and spoke softly. "Yes, my child. Continue to follow your heart and trust that I am leading you down the right path despite all the obstacles. You have been through a lot—all your suffering, pain, and hurt—but it happened for a purpose. And I have been with you every step of the way."

Upon hearing these words spoken aloud by such a powerful being, peace returned to Vincent's soul.

"But it is important that you always put me first," God warned. "Not when it is convenient, not only when you are in trouble but always."

Vincent thought about his prayers during desperate times and knew he often only considered God when he needed help.

God spoke again in a gentle yet powerful way. "Do you pray out of fear or love?"

This question made Vincent's heart skip a beat. For years, he had only prayed out of fear—fear for what would happen if he strayed too far away from God's path or if retribution should find its way into his life.

"I know why you do this," God said, gently answering Vincent's silent response. "It is because you are afraid that if you don't obey me or ask for my help when needed, I will abandon you."

It was startling to hear—and feel—God speaking to him. Part of Vincent wanted to shrink and hide, but a larger part wanted to continue this conversation with God. As he regained the ability to move, Vincent sat and looked at God.

Taking both of Vincent's hands in his own, God said, "My son, you must understand that your fears are unfounded. It is not fear which binds us together but love. Love is what gives us strength and hope even when things seem impossible."

Vincent's heart felt lighter as he heard those words knowing they were more than platitudes. They were truths meant to bring comfort during difficult times.

"The mistake you've made throughout your life has been relying solely on fear instead of turning towards me with open arms filled with love," God expressed to him. "This may seem hard to accept now but trust me. It will make all the difference beyond anything else."

Vincent nodded because what else could he do but agree with God? "I do trust you," he said.

"While it is important to follow my laws and teachings with respect, genuine devotion comes not just from following these rules but also through understanding them with love in your heart," God explained. "True faith requires both knowledge and emotion; without feeling deeply connected to me, no matter how much you may follow my ways, your prayers will remain empty words sent off listlessly into nothingness rather than heartfelt pleas destined for fulfillment."

Vincent had been waiting for this moment his entire life. He had spent countless hours in deep contemplation, striving to reach a higher understanding of the Universe and its creator. For years, Vincent had often felt so much anger towards God, believing he was not truly listening to his prayers. He had poured out his heart many nights as he struggled but still felt nothing but silence. Each time it only seemed to make him angrier, causing him to question why his cries weren't being answered or even acknowledged.

In moments of quiet contemplation, Vincent asked himself if he was wrong about God and that maybe something else was at work here. Still, it seemed impossible for him to accept this truth, even with the pain of unanswered prayers lingering in his heart. It felt like a wound that refused to heal no matter how hard he tried, and it only compounded with each tribulation that came into his life. And now, he finally stood face-to-face with God himself.

"My Lord," Vincent said softly, "I have many questions." He paused, unsure if he was permitted to question God.

God smiled knowingly and replied in a gentle voice that echoed throughout the enchanted room, "Go ahead, child. Ask whatever you desire."

Taking courage from these words, Vincent began speaking rapidly as all his doubts and questions came tumbling forth.

"Why did you create us?"
"What is our purpose here?"
"How can I help make this world better?"
"Is there really such a thing as free will, or are we just puppets on strings?"

As each question passed through his lips, it seemed like an eternity between them until, finally, they were all spoken aloud into the air around him.

God listened patiently without interruption until Vincent got out every question, then looked upon him warmly and with compassion. "My beloved son," he said tenderly, "your inquisitiveness shall be rewarded. Take solace knowing that even if you cannot see every answer now, eventually, your journey will lead you closer towards your truth."

Vincent remained silent, but those wise words stirred something deep inside him. Perhaps it was hope or faith or both combined. He then asked, "But God, why do you deny so many people the things they pray for?"

God nodded knowingly. "My son, all people desire something from time to time that they believe will make

THE BUDDHA WHO DROVE A BENTLEY

their lives better or easier; however, sometimes it is not yet time for them to receive those things they seek."

It made sense when God spoke it, but Vincent had never believed others when they offered a similar response to his question.

"When you are presented with a choice or opportunity," continued God solemnly, "you must remember that your choices should always be guided by love rather than selfishness or greed; if you choose out of love, there is no wrong decision."

"But Lord," protested Vincent helplessly, "how do I know which decisions will benefit me most? How do I know what you want me to do?"

God smiled again at his earnestness and replied kindly, "You see, my son, although some may find temporary relief or pleasure through certain decisions in life, it is only through my guidance one can experience true joy and contentment. That is why it's important to remember that you remain open-minded whenever you are faced with difficult decisions so your heart can lead you toward my best plan for your future. You must never doubt me, never."

Vincent was silent as he contemplated these words before asking meekly, "So how can I trust your plan when things seem uncertain? What assurance do I have that you really know what's best for us? "

God's expression softened even further at Vincent's question. "The truth is no matter how much faith you put in me, no matter how often things might seem to be against you, if you hold fast to hope—even when everything else fails—you'll soon realize how amazing my plans are. Because although they may not give you exactly what you want at first glance, they always provide something greater. But you must trust me and have absolute faith."

Vincent felt an inner peace as he listened to the divine words. The words resonated deeply within him as if they had been embedded into his very being since birth. Awe and admiration for the power of divine grace surrounding him filled his entire being. It felt like he was suspended between heaven and earth, caught in a moment of perfect stillness and harmony.

With his smile ever-present, God said, "My child, you were put on this earth for a reason—you are not an accident. It is my wish that you live your life according to my teachings so that you may find joy and fulfillment in all its forms. I want nothing more than for you to be happy, healthy, and safe throughout your journey here on Earth." In a warning tone, God added, "You have resisted me for too long."

Vincent swallowed hard, nodding.

God continued speaking, explaining the importance of following his will if one was truly seeking happiness and peace of mind. "It is not enough simply to believe in me; one must follow my commandments as well, lest they suffer the consequences of their actions both now and later on down the road when judgment day comes."

Judgment day, Vincent thought. *Is this mine?*

God heard Vincent's concern, though he declined to answer. "At times, staying true to my word will be difficult, but you must not waver if you want an eternity filled with joy rather than sorrow. Please remember that I want only what's best for you despite your human nature, which often leads you astray. I understand that breaking away from societal pressures is hard work at times, but trust me, it will always pay off greatly in the end."

Suddenly, Vincent felt like the world was caving in on him—everything around him became pitch black and eerily silent. Not even God's presence was with him. His heart pounded with anticipation, and his palms began to sweat with anxiety as he waited for something to happen.

Then, it all changed: the darkness lifted, and a dazzlingly bright light filled the space around him.

Vincent squinted and rubbed his eyes but could not see anything. The blinding brightness surrounded him—it was almost as if he were suspended in complete nothingness. He tried to move his arms or legs to orient himself in this strange place, but nothing happened. There were no walls or furniture he could feel, just an ever-present light that seemed to swallow everything around him. It was like being in a dream he couldn't wake up from, no matter how hard he tried. He was scared and confused at the same time.

"Help!" Vincent tried calling out, but the white void muffled his voice.

After what felt like hours of confusion and despair, Vincent finally felt a subtle presence in the air that was both comforting and calming at the same time.

"Have faith, my loyal servant," God said, "for your journey has come to an end. You must now choose whether to stay here or return home." His voice echoed loudly through space like thunder yet still gentle enough for an infant's ears. "Your decision will determine mankind's fate forevermore," he added solemnly.

Silence filled the air again while God waited patiently for what would soon become Vincent's eternal choice.

There was a lot for Vincent to consider. On the one hand, he could be with God in heaven and live a peaceful, eternal life without suffering or pain. On the other hand, he had the opportunity to return to earth and reunite with his beloved family.

The gravity of Vincent's choice was overwhelming. He understood that this wasn't a simple binary choice between two options but a decision that could potentially have far-reaching consequences. As his mind raced through all the pros and cons, he felt torn.

Vincent knew that if he chose Heaven, he would be in a place with no pain, suffering, or sorrow—where love and joy abound. A vision of him in heaven appeared in his mind: The sun shone brightly on lush wildflowers in meadows, and birdsong filled the air. The sky was so blue that it seemed to reach the heavens, and he could feel the warmth of a gentle breeze on his skin. Rolling hills stretched to the horizon, providing beautiful views at every turn. Beauty and wonders beyond compare were everywhere he looked—from majestic mountains and vast oceans with rolling waves to an endless array of stars filling the night sky.

This vision showed Vincent that Heaven was also a place with never-ending abundance in every form imaginable: food, wealth, creativity, and knowledge—all were available in infinite quantities there. People were smiling—laughter comes easy when you know all your worries have been banished.

Above all else, there was love for one another and for God, who resided in all the hearts there with an everlasting bond that could never be broken or weakened by any force on Earth.

Vincent knew that, although the path to heavenly bliss may be easier and more comfortable, his true destiny was back home with his family. He was determined to use the newfound wisdom he had acquired during his journey to make a positive difference in the world. Although it may be difficult and the outcome uncertain, he was prepared to face any obstacles that came his way.

Inspiring stories of people who changed the course of history by following their dreams and passions gave

Vincent strength. He believed that no matter how small or insignificant one person's actions are, they can still have a tremendous impact on the world around them.

As he weighed his decision to return, Vincent envisioned a better future for all, where every individual's contribution counts towards making a difference. He was ready to take action and fight for what he believed in. With courage and determination, he would strive to create a society that values equality and justice for everyone.

The knowledge and experience Vincent gained on his journey would help him to help others realize their potential. He hoped to build a brighter future for generations to come.

Vincent had made his decision...

Heaviness suddenly filled Vincent's heart as he left the vision of Heaven. Even though he was hopeful about returning home, he somehow knew the transition from the paradise he had been living in back to his life would be difficult.

The path down from the space he shared with God seemed endless and arduous, yet Vincent trudged onwards, knowing it had to be done. Angels singing beautiful songs in his honor escorted him. The sweet melody kept Vincent's spirits up, but it did little to ease the pain of parting with his visions of Heaven's beauty.

Finally, after what felt like an eternity of travel, Vincent reached the final stage before returning to his physical body on Earth. It was a brief moment where he could look back at all his experiences in the mysterious jungle he'd called home for weeks and take stock of all he had learned there. He thought fondly of all the wonderful people and the incredible sights he had seen. Much of that would stay with him forever, even though he was physically leaving that paradise behind.

The time came for Vincent to enter the portal back into earthly existence. As soon as he stepped inside its glittering threshold, an overwhelming wave of emotions filled his entire being—fear, confusion, and excitement swirled within him at once so quickly it almost made him dizzy. This was it; he was going home. Nothing would ever be quite the same again.

Chapter Seventeen

*I know what it is to be in need, and I know what it is
to have plenty. I have learned the secret of being content in
any and every situation, whether well fed or hungry,
whether living in plenty or in want. I can do all
this through him who gives me strength.*

—Philippians 4:12-13

Vincent heard his surroundings before he saw them. *Beep, beep, beep.* He briefly thought he was back in the hospital during his father's final days but then realized he wasn't reliving a memory.

When Vincent opened his eyes, he couldn't see anything clearly. He was definitely in a hospital room with sunlight streaming through a window. Besides the beeping, people were murmuring nearby. Slowly, his vision cleared, and he recognized his family and friends gathered around him.

How did I get here? Suddenly, he remembered everything: The car speeding out of control at 133 miles per hour, hearing a loud bang, and then feeling a jolt as the vehicle lost control. The next thing he remembered was careening off the road toward a tree. The vision felt as real as when it happened.

Vincent closed his eyes and braced for impact, but instead, a strong force pulled him out of the car. Suddenly, he was hovering in mid-air. He gasped as he looked around, his eyes adjusting to the bright light surrounding him. Everything was so surreal and peaceful, like a dream.

It was like Vincent was simultaneously gliding through the clouds yet walking on solid ground. Then, a grand entrance with two large wooden doors and intricately carved gold details appeared. He pushed through and found himself surrounded by lush gardens full of vibrant colors and unfamiliar fragrances. His heart beat faster as the reality of what was happening dawned on him. *I died.*

But he didn't die. Vincent was given a choice, and he chose to return.

Little by little, Vincent's reality came into focus. First, he noticed his throat was parched, as if he hadn't drunk anything for days. Then, he felt pressure against his wrist. When he looked down, he saw an IV line connected to it.

Vincent attempted to move but groaned in pain. He assumed he had been in the hospital for a while because his wife and daughters jumped to his side, overcome with emotion.

With tears of joy streaming down her face, his wife gently brushed her hand across his forehead as if trying to make sure he was really there. "We thought we had lost you," she whispered, tenderly caressing Vincent's face. "We have been praying for you for weeks after your accident." Unable to find other words to express her emotions, she silently held him.

His children stood quietly by, looking worriedly at their father. "It's okay," Vincent said with a hoarse voice. "I'm here now, and I plan on staying with all of you for a good while longer."

Vincent's mother joined his wife and children around his bed, frowning with worry. He knew this must have brought back painful memories of the final days she spent with his father.

Calm washed over her face as Vincent was about to comfort and reassure her. As if weeks—maybe years—of worry for him released at that moment, tears overflowed from her eyes. Her eyes spoke words of love and encouragement. "You have been through so much and achieved even more. I am proud of you for never giving up, especially now."

Vincent's heart swelled with emotion listening to his mother's words. No matter what happened next, he knew he could count on his fiercely loving family to stand by him until the very end. He smiled weakly at his mother before turning away from her gaze and closing his eyes for just a moment to prepare for whatever awaited him beyond this moment.

Peace washed over Vincent as he relived his near-death experience once again. He wanted to share his journey with his family, but it would have to wait until his throat wasn't so dry and it was easier to speak.

☥

It took a day, but when Vincent regained the ability to speak, he told his family about visiting a mystical paradise where he met beautiful, wise people who shared with him the knowledge and mission to improve himself and society's broken systems.

"The things I encountered also showed me visions of what people could achieve if they worked together in harmony," Vincent said to his captive audience. "Although it seemed like forever, in those few weeks, my teachers, the angels, revealed how I could use my life experiences to improve the world. They gave me insights into how all people are connected by our shared humanity and asked me to share this wisdom with others so they could find meaning and peace in their own lives too."

Vincent was relieved to see his family accept his story, so he continued. It took an entire afternoon, but Vincent retold his adventure to his family. There was something about sharing his experience that made it feel real, transforming it into a purpose that would drive him and inspire others.

Vincent knew now that fame or fortune didn't define greatness; it's found within oneself when one has fully committed themselves to do good for humanity out of love rather than ambition or desire for recognition. This was Vincent's highest calling now, and nothing could stop him from fulfilling it with every fiber of his being.

After his family had left for the night, Vincent saw a tall and luminous figure dressed in an ancient-looking saffron-colored robe walking in the hallway with a serene expression on its face. *Buddha?* His bald head glowed like the morning sun, radiating a golden light illuminating the entire corridor.

As the man walked past Vincent's room, he paused for a few seconds, flashing a gentle, knowing smile before disappearing into thin air.

Going Deeper

Throughout the book, Vincent met many guides who taught him valuable lessons. This guide provides insights and helpful suggestions to incorporate the wisdom into your life.

Chapter One

This story began during Vincent's youth. From early in his life, the capacity to overcome obstacles was second nature to him. His perseverance allowed him to achieve goal after goal after goal, overcoming insurmountable odds.

From an outside perspective, this boy from a poor, foreign neighborhood achieved the American dream. But at what cost? Did the life Vincent created fulfill him?

In what ways are you like Vincent? What adversaries have you had to overcome?

When you reach a point like Vincent did when he recklessly abandoned his life, it helps to pause and ask God for guidance.

Prayer for Wisdom and Discernment

Lord God, Your Word says you are a sun and a shield, you give grace and glory, and no good thing will you withhold from those who walk uprightly (Psalm 84:11). Lord, be my sun, shining your light on my path; and be my shield, protecting me from missteps and opposition along the way. I ask that you withhold nothing good from my life as I seek to walk uprightly. Grant me wisdom because your Word says if any of us lack wisdom, we should ask it of you, and you will give it generously and without finding fault in us (James 1:5). I need your wisdom, God, to know which way to turn and how to move forward. Give me clarity by opening or closing doors according to your absolute best for me. Still my heart to hear your gentle voice for your Word says your sheep hear your voice and follow you (John 10:27). Make your voice very clear to me through your Word, through the situations in my life, and through Godly counsel from those who are clearly living for you. It's in the all-knowing and ever-faithful name of Jesus that I pray this. Amen.[3]

3 Cindi McMenamin, "7 Prayers for When You Feel Lost in Life," Crosswalk.com, February 23, 2023, https://www.crosswalk.com/faith/prayer/prayers-for-when-you-feel-lost-in-life.html.

Chapter Two

Arriving in the new land, Vincent felt confused. Although he admired the beauty of his new surroundings and the joy of others around him, he felt disconnected.

Often, we find ourselves in unfamiliar situations. The natural reaction for many is to withdraw to a comfortable space. Have you ever visited a land where you couldn't speak the language? Or maybe you started a new job, and their methods were foreign? What is your inclination when you arrive in these unfamiliar circumstances?

Prayer for an Eternal Perspective

Lord, give me an eternal perspective. When I look around at what's happening in this world, I can often wonder where I fit in. I can begin to think that this life is all there is. But it's not. Your Word tells me to set my heart on things above, not on things of this earth (Colossians 3:2). Grant me the wisdom to seek first your kingdom and your righteousness (Matthew 6:33) and not to strive to make a name for myself in this world that will not last. Help me to store up for myself treasures in heaven, not here on earth where moth and rust destroy, and where thieves break in and steal (Matthew 6:19-21). Lord, remind me that promotion comes from God alone, who lifts up one and puts down another (Psalm 75:6-7). Jesus, help me to hide myself in you (Colossians 3:2-4) and to remember that "I have been crucified with Christ; and it is no longer I who live, but Christ lives in me; and the life which I now live in the flesh I live by faith in the Son of God, who loved me and gave Himself up for me" (Galatians 2:20 New American Standard Bible®).

Instead of looking for answers, help me to look to you as THE ANSWER to all I need and all I search for. In Jesus' capable name, I pray. Amen.[1]

Chapter Three

The conversation between Vincent and Julia reminds us of the importance of truth. Julia's message encourages us to pursue the truth not just for its own sake but as a way of being—to live with it as a guiding principle that brings greater clarity. Living through the lens of truth can be daunting, yet embracing this practice will ultimately bring us closer to our highest selves and lead us down a path of greater fulfillment.

"Sanctify them by the truth; your word is truth" (John 17:17). Living with truth as a core value is an essential ingredient to leading a fulfilled life. Its presence will bring us closer to our highest selves and helps us recognize the things that truly matter. Applying this layer of honesty to our lives allows conscious decision-making based on values and purpose. This way, we can lead lives filled with deeper connections and understanding. As Vincent and Julia discussed, living through the lens of truth is an invaluable lesson worth pursuing.

The goal should not be merely to search for the truth but also to *live by it*. When we integrate truth into our lives, it can lead to greater clarity. We then become empowered. Julia explained to Vincent, "If we strive to live true to ourselves, we will find peace, contentment, and fulfillment in life. Something that most people never experience."

Ultimately, living in truth can be a challenging yet rewarding journey. By embracing it as a central part of our lives, not only do we gain greater peace and contentment within ourselves, but we also open ourselves up to richer, more meaningful relationships with the people around us.

Prayer for Self-Truth (Based on Jeremiah 1:5.)

> Father God, I pray that you help me to always remember that you are the creator and author of life. You knew me long before I was born or even conceived. you wrote the story of my life before I was living in it, and you set out a purpose and a plan for me long ago. Lord, help me to accept the person that you made me to be, blessings, difficulties, and all. Help me to recognize the plans and purpose for my life and to know there is no purpose too big or too small in this world, as you are the one who gave it to me. In Jesus' name, I pray. Amen.[4]

Chapter Four

Isabella spoke to Vincent about how his suffering and attachments were related. "Attachment can manifest in various forms. For you, Vincent, it has been an attachment for accumulating material possessions and success."

It is easy to get caught up in consumerism: the need to buy the latest iPhone, replace your wardrobe to keep up with the latest fashion trends, purchase the latest model car, etc. Ad companies pay millions each year to make you

---

[4]   Ashley Adewuyi, "3 Short Prayers about Being Your True Self," THEOS Academy Powered by ROHO Ministry, accessed June 27, 2023, https://www.theosacademy.com/blogs/purpose/3-short-pr ayers-about-being-your-true-self.

want what they're selling. But as we saw with Vincent, possessions don't bring fulfillment.

Prayer to Avoid Accumulating Possessions

> Father, Materialism and consumerism constantly bombard us. I admit that I have been overtaken by the tidal wave of temptation to buy things that I do not need. Instead of budgeting for items, I have made impulse purchases. I ask you to help me when I face the temptation to buy things that I don't need or perhaps want because someone else has it. I may be tempted by materialism, but I do not have to act upon it and sin against you. Help me see these things clearly, Father. I trust that you provide all of my needs. I ask for you to help me steward my finances and help me to be content with what you have given me. Thank you for your grace to overcome this temptation and for always providing an escape for me. In Jesus's name, Amen.[5]

Chapter Five

Forgiveness is a powerful act. As Alexander Pope wrote, "To err is human; to forgive, divine.[6]" Gina reminded Vincent

5   Emily Rose Massey, "A Prayer against the Temptation of Materialism - Your Daily Prayer - July 14," Crosswalk.com, July 14, 2022, https://www.crosswalk.com/devotionals/your-daily-prayer/a-prayer-again st-the-temptation-of-materialism.html#:~:text=I%20 may%20be%20 tempted%20by,see%20these%20things%20clearly%2C%20Father.

6   Alexander Pope - to ERR is human; to forgive, divine. - brainyquote, accessed June 28, 2023, https://www.brainyquote.com/quotes/alexander_pope_101451.

of this. "I want you to understand that the journey toward freedom begins with one small step: forgiveness. Forgiving yourself may be difficult, but ultimately, it'll be worth it. Forgiveness is the only way out. Everyone deserves it, including you."

However simply stated, it is the truth. Who haven't you forgiven for wronging you? Or maybe it's yourself you need to give grace and forgiveness to.

Below are two short prayers you can use when you need help forgiving yourself or others.

Prayer to Forgive Yourself

Father, today I ask forgiveness of all the negative and harmful words I have spoken about myself. I do not want to abuse myself in such a way again. Transform my thoughts and let me understand how marvelously you made me. Change my habits so I use my tongue to speak hope and favor upon my life. In Jesus's name.[7]

Prayer to Forgive Others

Father, this is the day you have made; we will rejoice and be glad in it. Father, you hold the key to every heart on earth; we do not. Judgment for others is not in our hands and shouldn't be on our resumes. As we seek you more each day in prayer and in your Word, show us how to be forgiving in Christ. Cleanse us of our tendency to keep records of wrongs and reasons for blame. Let us not

---

[7] "15 Best Prayers for Forgiveness - Forgiving Others and for Yourself," Crosswalk.com, September 20, 2022, https://www.crosswalk.com/faith/prayer/4-prayers-for-forgiveness-for-sin-healing-and-others.html.

become people who shame others but show them how to be free through Christ. We want our lives to reflect your brightness, your grace, and your love. In Jesus's name, Amen.[5]

Chapter Six

We can let go of what no longer serves us, so our hearts are open to embracing whatever life brings fully at each moment. Letting go invites us to live with intention—to give up the need for control so we can experience freedom within.

The power of the Presence that can bring light into even the darkest places awakened Vincent. When we let go of our fears and doubts, we can find true freedom in each moment. The opportunity to experience life in all its richness and complexity blesses us.

Letting go does not mean giving up; it means allowing yourself to be at peace without trying to force a specific outcome or result. With each deep breath, open your heart and mind to see and accept all that is around you. Do not be afraid of change; lean into it as an opportunity for growth and transformation. Release your worries, doubts, fears, and regrets, and allow yourself to be present in each moment.

This is the power of letting go; it frees us from our idea of how things are supposed to be and opens us up to live life with authenticity. As we surrender into this space, we can experience a deep inner peace that radiates outward, creating joy and abundance. May you find the courage to let go and open your heart to all life has to offer.

THE BUDDHA WHO DROVE A BENTLEY

Prayer for Letting Go

Heavenly Father, I come before you today to ask for your help in letting go of the things that are holding me back. I know that I cannot do this on my own, and I need your strength and guidance to move forward. Help me to release any hurt, pain, and bitterness that I am holding onto and to forgive those who have wronged me. Give me the courage and wisdom to make the necessary changes in my life and to trust in your plan for me. I pray that you would fill me with your peace, love, and joy and that I would experience the freedom that comes from surrendering all to you. Thank you for your faithfulness and grace and for always being with me through every trial and struggle. I trust in your goodness, and I give you all the praise and glory. In Jesus's Name, Amen.[8]

Chapter Seven

Olivia spoke passionately about the beauty of the land and its deep connection to our past, present, and future. Her words remind us to be thankful for what the earth has given us and respect it by caring for it. Honoring Nature's gift with reverence, humility, and appreciation is essential. We need to remember the stories of those who came before us—their joys, sorrows, and struggles—so we can continue to cherish the magnificent land for many generations.

The sun provides warmth, light, and nourishment. It gives energy, helps plants grow, and brings life to our world.

---

8   Daniel, "11 Prayers for Letting Go – How to Move on & Let God Lead You," DAILY EFFECTIVE PRAYER, June 1, 2023, https://www.dailyeffectiveprayer.org/prayers-for-letting-go/.

Being outdoors can be incredibly calming and refreshing, allowing us to take a break from the hustle and bustle of everyday life. Enjoying nature by walking in the park or simply sitting outside is a therapeutic way to clear our minds and appreciate the beauty surrounding us.

Olivia's message is a reminder of why we should all love this earth so much: it's beautiful, resilient, full of history, and serves as an inspiration. No matter how challenging life may seem, we can take solace in knowing that our home is here to stay—where the mountains reach into the sky, where wildlife flourishes, and Mother Nature abounds—forever reminding us just how lucky we are to call this our home.

Prayer for the Earth

> O God, who in six days made Heaven and Earth and gave Earth to your children for safekeeping, I make my prayer to you to guard, enlighten and inspire our minds and our bodies so that we are fit for this great task. I recognize how often my sins have contributed to the destruction of this wonderful gift that you have given us. Let me now resolve to work to keep my soul, my body, and all that surrounds it unspoiled and a garden worthy of your Majesty. Amen.[9]

---

[9] "16 Powerful Prayers for the Earth," ConnectUS, June 17, 2020, https://connectusfund.org/16-powerful-prayers-for-the-earth#:~:text=Prayer%20for%20the%20Earth&text=Let%20me%20now%20resolve%20to,Amen.

Chapter Eight

Too often, people get caught up in the rat race of life and forget to appreciate the beauty around them. It's crucial to take a step back from the hustle and bustle of everyday life and recognize what truly matters: relationships, making genuine connections with others, and discovering who we are as individuals.

Staying focused on what matters most can be challenging in a world full of distractions. It's easy to get caught up in the daily grind and lose sight of our true purpose and potential.

This issue is exacerbated as the pace of life continues to accelerate, and technology allows us to access virtually every imaginable resource. Advancements in technology have made everything more accessible but also more demanding than ever before. From communication with others world-wide via the internet or reaching distant places by plane quickly, our lives have been filled with expectations to stay connected 24/7 while desperately working to stay ahead of the competition and make the most money.

Unfortunately, many continue in the same patterns that have kept them from achieving their potential and living a happy, fulfilling life. They rush through life, caught up in the never-ending cycle of work and worry. Constantly bombarded with information overload, they forget to take time for themselves, disconnect from technology, or explore ways to develop their spiritual awareness. This makes it difficult to separate what is true and valuable from what simply takes up space in their heads.

It's important to slow down and enjoy the views life offers. As wise shamans have said, "Take a break from your busy schedule every now and then and allow yourself to daydream, reflect on your journey so far, and be mindful of the beauty that surrounds you." Without a sense of clarity or purpose, it can be hard to feel contentment or satisfaction with life. This leads to feelings of stress, frustration, and unhappiness that many people struggle with on a daily basis.

Vincent's spiritual guide knew he had forgotten one key life lesson: We are here to share love and connection. We're meant to create meaningful relationships with each other and foster a sense of belonging that transcends place or time. Life isn't about accumulating wealth and status but about living an abundant life filled with joy, kindness, and compassion.

True abundance comes from within rather than without. Sometimes, we need to be reminded that no amount of money or possessions can bring as much lasting happiness as the simple act of giving love and telling a loved one how much they mean to us.

It's important to listen closely to these teachings if we want to find true peace within ourselves. By stepping back and slowing down, we can connect with our innermost selves—the Buddha or Jesus inside us all—allowing us to become more fully realized people. So let's remember this wise shamanic advice and take a moment to be still, appreciate life's beauty, and find inner peace.

Prayer for Peace of Mind

Lord Jesus, we ask you to give us all-around peace in our mind, body, soul, and spirit. We want you to heal and remove everything that is causing stress, grief, and sorrow in our lives. Please guide our path through life and make our enemies be at peace with us. Let your peace reign in our family, at our place of work, businesses, and everything we lay our hands on. Let your angels of peace go ahead of us when we go out and stay by our side when we return. In Jesus' name, Amen.[10]

Chapter Nine

Family is the key to true fulfillment. It's not only something we need but also something we should be deeply grateful for. Show gratitude for them by cherishing every moment spent with them, and don't take this precious gift for granted. Life is too short not to appreciate the people who are unconditionally by our side. So let us never forget how important family truly is in our lives.

Having a family brings such a richness to life that simply cannot be replaced. It creates a safe haven of love and support that can hold us up when everything else seems to crumble. The importance of having a family will never fade away, as its effects on our lives will remain for eternity.

Family is one of the greatest gifts life can offer. So embrace it with all your heart and cherish every moment. It's an invaluable source of support, understanding, comfort, and joy that can bring immense fulfillment to life no matter what comes our way. Let us be ever-grateful for this special bond and nurture it throughout our lives.

At the end of our lives, when we finally come to terms with our mortality, there is nothing more important than being surrounded by those who love us. All of the material possessions and achievements we have accumulated over the years mean nothing compared to having the warmth

---

[10] "Calmness Prayers," Xavier University, accessed June 27, 2023, https://www.xavier.edu/jesuitresource/online-resources/prayer-index/calmness-prayers#:~:text=Lord%20Jesus%2C%20we%20ask%20you,be%20at%20peace%20with%20us.

and companionship of family. Knowing their presence will bring comfort during our last moments brings a profound peace and solace that isn't found anywhere else.

When we look back on our life, we will remember these precious, tender moments spent with those who cherish us most. So, as you go through your days, remember to always make time for loved ones. Because when it is all said and done, they are truly what matters most.

Prayer for Family

Father, help us to remember that we are not just individuals out to achieve our own agendas. You have joined us together as a family; unite our hearts in love. Remind us that we are stronger together. Show us how to love each other sacrificially, graciously, and generously every day. May we serve each other, performing even the smallest acts of kindness for one another without complaint or scorekeeping. We ask that our love for one another reflect Christ's sacrificial and unconditional love so that others will look at our home and our family and see you. Let our love for one another draw others to know your love for them.[11]

Chapter Ten

Truth, or the pursuit of it, lies at the heart of joy. But how do we recognize it? How can we tap into and draw on its power to make a meaningful difference in our lives? Elaina's

---

[11] Heather C. King, "7 Prayers for Your Home and Family," Heather C. King - Room to Breathe, September 18, 2014, https://heathercking. org/2014/09/17/7-prayers-for-your-home-and-family/.

spiritual light offers an answer: We do it by understanding the story within us.

Your inner story may be one of pain, suffering, and confusion, but it is also one of hope, beauty, and resilience. It is a narrative that speaks of courage in the face of adversity, love despite fear, and faith even in moments of despair. By recognizing this story within ourselves, we can unlock a powerful source of strength and comfort.

We all have something inside us that guides our truth. Whether we call it intuition, wisdom, or divine guidance, this inner knowing is a powerful force that has the potential to lead us in the right direction. Elaina's spiritual light encourages us to pay attention to these whispers and follow their lead—they will bring us closer to our true purpose in life.

Prayer for Wisdom and Discernment

> Lord, Thank you for the people you have divinely placed in my life who speak holy truth, love, and words of wisdom. Give me a heart of discernment to know when you are using someone to speak instruction into my heart and my circumstances, and give me the strength and courage to follow through with that advice, even when it's hard. Fill me with peace in knowing that even if I take a wrong turn, your purpose will prevail. In Jesus's Name, Amen.[12]

---

[12] Tracie Miles, "15 Prayers for Guidance and Wisdom When You Need Direction from God," Crosswalk.com, January 31, 2023, https://www.crosswalk.com/faith/prayer/5-prayers-for-guidance-receive-god-s-direction-and-wisdom.html.

Chapter Eleven

Honoring your feelings lets you stay connected to your intuition and wisdom. It is a way of cultivating self-awareness and understanding yourself deeper.

When we become aware of our emotions, we can more easily identify their origin, what triggers them, and how we can best cope with them. This greater awareness enables us to make conscious choices about how we respond at any given moment. Honoring our feelings helps us develop the capacity to trust ourselves and honor who we are without judgment or criticism.

As we move through life, staying true to ourselves can help shift our focus from external validation towards meaningful internal growth that comes from within. Honoring our feelings is essential for living an authentic life full of joy, compassion, and fulfillment.

Acknowledging our feelings also allows us to form deeper connections with those around us. By being open to our emotions, we can more easily empathize with others and understand their feelings. This empathy creates a stronger bond between people, opening doors for meaningful conversations and deeper relationships.

It's not easy to honor your feelings, but it is worth the effort. When you take the time to listen to what your heart and soul tell you, it can feel like you are tapping into a secret wisdom that will lead you to a life of contentment and harmony. When we honor our feelings, we free ourselves from limiting beliefs and find the courage to live in alignment with who we are.

Prayer to Honor Emotions

Lord, you are not only the Creator of me but of my emotions as well. Forgive me for those times that I have tried to deny what I am feeling and for those times that I have allowed my emotions to control me. Help me to grow to emotional maturity. I understand that there is a time and a place for even my emotions. Give me wisdom in knowing when the proper time and place is to show them. Thank you, Lord.[13]

Chapter Twelve

Mia's advice to Vincent is wise and timeless. Spending time with people who share a common goal can bring back moments of joy, peace, and comfort. This could be as simple as taking an hour to talk about your dreams or ambitions over coffee. Or maybe it's getting together for a group workout to stay motivated or having a weekly potluck at each other's houses. The possibilities are endless!

No matter what you choose to do, the key is to make sure that your friendship circle nurtures your soul. It's important to find someone who understands where you're coming from and supports the direction of your journey—whether it's finding success through business ventures or pursuing a happier lifestyle through meditation. These relationships will provide guidance, help, and comfort in times of struggle, and that's when real growth begins.

---

[13] Tonia Slimm, "We Are Emotional Beings – Ecclesiastes 3:4," Growing with God, March 31, 2020, https://scenichillsblvd.wordpress.com/2020/03/31/we-are-emotional-beings-ecclesiastes-34/.

Mia's advice is also a reminder to stay connected to your passions and ambitions. If you can do that alongside friends who share the same values, then you can't go wrong!

A Prayer for Friendship

I give thanks for my friends, for connection and laughter, for comfort and strength, for encouragement and unity, for forgiveness and grace, for celebration and joy. They are so many things to me, such a rich tapestry of blessings woven through my life. Thank you. Amen.[14]

Chapter Thirteen

Jesus saw giving as a way of receiving blessings in return. He noted that generosity should not be done out of a sense of obligation but out of genuine kindness and love. As an advocate for those with less, he recognized the importance of reaching out to help those who need it most. Jesus believed that if individuals are generous with what they have been blessed with, then even more blessings would come their way in return.

Throughout his ministry, Jesus exemplified this idea by feeding five thousand people from five loaves and two fish and visiting those who were sick or suffering from poverty or other forms of adversity (Matthew 14:13-21). He also told parables about individuals who helped others regardless of their social status or position, such as The Parable of the Good Samaritan (Luke 10:25-37) and The Rich Man

---

14   "23 Prayers to Send Love and Healing to a Friend Going through a Hard Time," Woman's Day, June 13, 2023, https://www.womansday.com/relationships/family-friends/g28423074/prayers-for-a-friend/?slide=9.

and Lazarus (Luke 16:19-31). These stories emphasize how beneficial it can be for people to give what they can to help others in need.

Ultimately, Jesus's message was clear: While our own needs must always come first, we should also strive to share our resources with those less fortunate than us and help them wherever we can. Doing so reinforces the power of abundance by demonstrating faithfulness in providing for one another's needs when times are hard, even when we have little. It also teaches us that though our earthly blessings may eventually run out, plenty of provisions are available through God's infinite grace when we practice giving generously with a kind heart and open mind.

A Prayer for Generosity

> My Righteous God, you created us, male and female, in your image. Because we are made in your image, we are made to reflect your giving and generous nature. Therefore, we ask that you mold us to better reflect this image. Shape our hearts, minds, and souls so that we might learn to give as freely as you give. For you are a God who holds nothing back but lays down even your own life for us. Amen.[15]

Chapter Fourteen

Taking control over mortality-related fears allows us to experience true freedom and incredible energy levels. Letting

---

[15]   "10 Powerful Prayers for Generosity," ConnectUS, May 26, 2020, https://connectusfund.org/10-powerful-prayers-for-generosity.

go of that fear empowers us to strive toward unknown horizons. It allows us to conquer every obstacle we encounter through a journey called life.

Sometimes, this results in achieving goals others deem impossible due to a lack of courage or low self-belief. It also gives us new clarity, allowing us to see situations from different perspectives and make better decisions.

This leads us closer to desired outcomes while

- unveiling the hidden potential within our hearts,
- opening doors we thought had closed forever,
- giving us a chance further develop our skills, and
- enabling us to reach the highest level possible throughout our lifetime.

We can leave behind a legacy that inspires future generations to explore unknown boundaries. All these results form a basis for individuals to gain complete control over their destiny, allowing them to live the fullest version possible.

Prayer for Accepting Mortality

Dear Lord, we will face many terrifying events throughout this life, but may we never forget that the ultimate victory belongs to you. Through your sacrifice, death has been defeated. As we continue to walk in your truth, help us to set our eyes on Heavenly things. Amen.[16]

---

[16] Rachel Dawson, "10 Prayers for the Dying (and the Mourning)," Crosswalk.com, August 25, 2021, https://www.crosswalk.com/faith/prayer/6-prayers-for-the-dying-and-the-mourning.html.

Chapter Fifteen

Caterina and Vincent discussed releasing the need to judge and accepting the fact you can't control anyone except yourself. "I have seen too many people try to change the world around them without ever understanding that one cannot change another person's heart. We may think we're playing a part in helping others, but ultimately, they must decide who they want to be on their own. The only thing anyone can do is love and accept those around them as they are." In other words, to release judgment, you have to love someone unconditionally.

This leads us to ask, What is unconditional love? Many associate it with their love for a spouse, child, or parent. According to Psych Central, "Unconditional love is when you love someone no matter what they do and have no expectation of repayment. It means you love someone for who they are, with no strings attached."[17]

But Caterina described it best when she told Vincent, "Love means allowing others the freedom to make their own choices while still being accepted and appreciated." This means unconditional love is extended to all people, not just those we are close to.

Who do you love unconditionally? Or a better question is, who don't you love unconditionally?

Prayer to Love Unconditionally

Dear Lord, Please help us to love our neighbors and to be kind to them. Help us not to show favoritism to those

---

[17] Janelle Cox, "Unconditional Love: What It Is and How to Find It," Psych Central, October 26, 2022, https://psychcentral.com/lib/soulmates-and-unconditional-love.

whom you put in our lives. Help us to love our families and friends. Help us to treat them with respect and love. Lord, we pray you instill your unconditional love in our hearts. Help us to carry that love and compassion everywhere we go. In Jesus's name, Amen.[18]

Chapter Sixteen

Vincent spent many years of his life praying out of fear and being angry with God for unanswered prayers. When Vincent admitted this, God responded, "I know why you do this. It is because you are afraid that if you don't obey me or ask for my help when needed, I will abandon you."

God knows what's in our hearts, even in the moments when we feel like he's abandoned us. But he has always had a plan for us, and it is our duty to learn to accept that plan. Pray to God out of love, not fear. He will reveal your path at the correct time. It is our responsibility to keep our faith in him and wait patiently for his answers.

But even when it feels like answers aren't forthcoming, God gives us gifts in the form of love, beauty, peace, and joy. He gives us strength and courage when we are faced with difficult times and also provides opportunities for personal growth and transformation when we least expect it. Our lives are enriched as we open ourselves up to receive these blessings from God.

By reflecting on our lives and individual goals, we begin to recognize what God offers. It could be a feeling of security through a steady job or financial stability, meaningful

---

[18] "Prayer - Unconditional Love," Godly Woman Daily, October 21, 2013, http://www.godlywoman.co/2013/09/prayer-unconditional-love.html.

relationships with loved ones, or being able to travel and explore new places. We also have moments alone where we can quietly reflect on our journey thus far and nurture our spiritual side in prayer or meditation.

When we realize how God has blessed us with all these possibilities, there is no limit to what life can offer. As long as we keep an open heart and stay true to his path, there will always be something new around the corner waiting for us if only we take some time to seek it.

Great rewards—physical and emotional abundance—come with faith in his divine plan. Believing that God has provided for us will make all of life's challenges just a little bit easier.

A Prayer for God's Will

Lord God, You have taught us that you have a plan for each one of us. Your hand guides our steps and provides us with all we need. Because you are good, you want only the best for us. Good and gracious God, I ask that your pathway will become manifest in my life. Help me to walk in the paths that you have laid out in front of me and lead me through the narrow gate. Amen.[19]

Chapter Seventeen

Vincent learned many lessons while he was unconscious in the hospital room, surrounded by his family. He had a choice, though, that extended beyond the choice God had

---

[19] "10 Powerful Prayers for God's Will," ConnectUS, May 28, 2021, https://connectusfund.org/10-powerful-prayers-for-gods-will.

given him: to return to his old ways or take a new path that could lead to greater happiness and fulfillment.

When in your life have you been at a crossroads? Did you make the easy choice? Or did you take the time needed to make the best choice for yourself?

As you come to these moments in your life, will you take the lessons learned and apply them or return to your old ways, continuing a possibly unfulfilling life?

A Prayer for a New Season

Dear Heavenly Father, please be with me, I pray, as I move on from the old to the new. The joy, memories, and hardships of the last season of my life are behind me. Help me to leave them there, Lord, and not carry them with me into this new season. Help me to let go of all hurts, anger, and grudges and see all people as the blessing they are, your children. Thank you, Lord, for this opportunity to begin this new adventure with you. In Jesus's name, I pray, Amen.[20]

Conclusion

No matter what we face in life, God is always with us and willing to fulfill his promises of abundance. All we have to do is believe and surrender our burdens into his loving arms.

With God on our side, no obstacle is too big to overcome and no challenge too great to conquer; God's love

---

20 "10 Powerful Prayers for Moving on and Letting Go," ConnectUS, May 27, 2020, https://connectusfund.org/10-powerful-prayers-for-moving-on-and-letting-go.

and mercy will be there until the end of time. May we all hold onto the promise of his faithfulness even when times are tough.

> *But blessed is the one who trusts in the Lord, whose confidence is in him. They will be like a tree planted by the water that sends out its roots by the stream. It does not fear when heat comes; its leaves are always green. It has no worries in a year of drought and never fails to bear fruit.*
> —Jeremiah 17:7-8

Acknowledgments

I would like to express my heartfelt gratitude to the incredible individuals who have played an instrumental role in making this book a reality. First and foremost, I want to thank my beautiful family for their unwavering love and support throughout this journey.

To Gina, my beloved wife: You have been my rock and anchor throughout this incredible journey. Your unwavering belief in me, even when self-doubt threatened to consume my every thought, has bolstered my spirit and fortified my resolve. Your love, patience, and unfaltering support have given me the courage to face the challenges that writing this story presented. You have illuminated my path with your unshakeable faith in God's plan for our lives, reminding me that purpose can emerge from suffering and that his glory will prevail.

To Julia, my eldest daughter: Your boundless curiosity and persistent determination has inspired me beyond measure. Your relentless pursuit of knowledge and zest for life reminds me of the infinite possibilities that lie within our grasp. Your belief in my abilities, even during the most trying times, has propelled me forward.

To Isabella, my middle daughter: Your compassionate soul and empathetic nature have touched the lives of many, including mine. Your constant support and understanding during the countless hours I spent lost in the words of this story have been a guiding light. Your gentle presence and warm heart have brought solace to my weary spirit, reminding me of the beauty that exists in the world.

To Olivia, my youngest daughter: Your infectious laughter and irrepressible spirit have been a constant source of joy and inspiration. Your belief in my storytelling abilities, even when doubts consumed me, has given me the strength to persevere. Your innocent wisdom and limitless imagination have reminded me of the power of dreams and the importance of sharing them with others.

I am immensely grateful to my immediate family, who have always been there for me. To my two sisters, Marilena and Cristina, and my older brother, Massimo: Your guidance and love have been invaluable.

To my nephews, Cristian Hubbard, Vincent Renda, and Luca Popolizio, and my nieces, Tatiana Tronco and Cecilia Popolizio: Your youthful energy inspires me every day.

And to my dear mother, Lucia: Thank you for your unconditional care and support.

To my late father, Carlo Tronco, the first author in our family: Thank you for taking so many risks in life to start us on this amazing journey.

I extend my heartfelt appreciation to my in-laws, Luigi and Catherine Sainato, my sister-in-law, Elaina Renda, and brothers-in-law, Vincent Renda and Frank Popolizio Jr., for embracing me as part of their family and for their constant encouragement.

A special mention goes to my extended family, who have shown me mercy, grace, and forgiveness, even during times when I felt undeserving. Your love and acceptance have touched my heart deeply.

To all my friends and coworkers: Thank you for your guidance and support throughout this writing process. Your encouragement and belief in my abilities have been instrumental in bringing this book to fruition.

Lastly, I want to express my profound gratitude to God for blessing me with this life and for showing me the beauty in every moment. Through all the pain and suffering, I have learned that with God by my side, anything is possible.

To all of you, my family, friends, and loved ones: I cannot find adequate words to express the depth of my love and appreciation. Thank you for being a part of my life and for enriching this journey with your presence.

About Alessandro Tronco

Alessandro Tronco is living proof that the American Dream still exists. Born in Sicily, he immigrated to the United States at only six years old with nothing but his family's hopes and dreams to guide him. After spending nearly a decade here, Alessandro returned to Sicily for six months and then returned to America by himself at fifteen years old with only five dollars in his pocket. Lack of experience and means didn't stop him from chasing his ambitions. He attended Siena College and then began working as a Financial Advisor for Northwestern Mutual, rising quickly through the ranks to become one of the youngest Managing Partners in the company's 166-year history. Through hard work and determination, Alessandro has gone from having only five dollars to his name to a success story.

Alessandro is a compassionate philanthropist, hard-working professional, and committed believer. He has dedicated his life to giving back to the community, supporting charitable organizations, and helping those in need. His unwavering faith helps guide him through difficult times, and his passion for justice serves as an example for others. Alessandro's enthusiasm for bettering the world sets him apart from others—he truly puts his heart into everything he does. When he isn't lending a hand to the less fortunate, Alessandro can be found reading uplifting books or enjoying time with family and friends. His zest for life inspires everyone around him!

Today, Alessandro is happily married to Gina and has three lovely daughters—Julia, Isabella, and Olivia. He continues to be a shining example that anyone can reach their goals and live out the American Dream with enough perseverance.

Connect with Alessandro at
TheBuddhaWhoDroveaBentley.com

ALESSANDRO WANTS TO CONNECT WITH YOU

Are you ready to live your most authentic life, find true happiness, and have it all?

Follow him on your favorite social media platforms.

TheBuddhaWhoDroveABentley.com

KEYNOTE SPEAKER

Alessandro Tronco is proof that with enough perseverance anyone can reach their goals and live out the American Dream.

He is a compassionate philanthropist, hardworking professional, and committed believer. He has dedicated his life to giving back to the community, supporting charitable organizations, and helping those in need.

START THE CONVERSATION TODAY

WORK WITH ALESSANDRO ONE-ON-ONE

ALESSANDRO'S ENTHUSIASM FOR BETTERING THE WORLD SETS HIM APART FROM OTHERS—HE TRULY PUTS HIS HEART INTO EVERYTHING HE DOES.

GET PERSONAL COACHING FROM ALESSANDRO AND EXPERIENCE FOR YOURSELF HOW HIS ZEST FOR LIFE INSPIRES EVERYONE AROUND HIM!

TheBuddhaWhoDroveABentley.com/Apply

About Gina Tronco

 Alessandro's childhood sweet-heart became his wife. Together with Gina, the couple decided to lift up others with their stories. Gina's book, *Why Is This Happening to Me?*, helps people to trust God when their lives feel out of control.

While actively involved in her community, she frequently participates in charity events and provides help to others like her who are facing health or marital struggles. Gina is also the 2023 Leukemia and Lymphoma Society Visionary of the Year for their home state of New York.

Can you Trust God When your World is Falling Apart?

High school sweethearts, perfect family, excelling career, extravagant trips, a beautiful home, Gina and Alex seemed to have it all—until the vacation that changed everything.

Gina received two types of news no woman wants to hear:

"I've been having multiple affairs throughout the past fifteen years."

"You have stage 2 breast cancer."

The confession from her husband and the diagnosis from her doctor blew up Gina's world.

The truth is we all receive unwanted news at some point in our lives. According to *Psych Central*, just under fifty percent of people in a monogamous relationship have had affairs. And the American Cancer Society estimates nearly 300,000 new breast cancer diagnoses in women every year. You may never have received this specific bad news, but at some time in your life, chances are you've asked yourself, "Why is this happening to me?"

Despite the tragedies, Gina found a way forward. She reveals a proven process to discover true hope and healing.

This book will show you how to:

- Recognize your current trial is part of a much bigger story.
- Trust God's plan for your life so that you realize you're not alone.
- Forgive the unforgivable so that you walk lighter and love deeper.

Is your world falling apart? If so, it's time to create a better future starting today.

Connect with Gina at WhyIsThisHappening.net

About Spirit Water

Alessandro and his wife, Gina, are very health-conscious and environmentally aware. In an effort to promote this lifestyle worldwide, they partnered with others to create Spirit Water, a flavored water company that focuses on uplifting souls and saving the planet.

Spirit is a company that envisions a world where everyone is healthy and thriving, and every sip of our flavored water is a step toward a better future. Good health and a better world go hand in hand, and we are committed to using our flavored water products to promote both.

We use only the finest, all-natural ingredients in sustainable packaging and support initiatives promoting health, wellness, and sustainability. With every sip of Spirit Water, we encourage people to embrace a healthier, more conscious way of living and to join us in creating a brighter future for all.

Discover more at SpiritWaterInc.com

EVERY SIP OF OUR FLAVORED WATER IS A STEP TOWARD A BETTER FUTURE. WE BELIEVE THAT GOOD HEALTH AND A BETTER WORLD GO HAND IN HAND

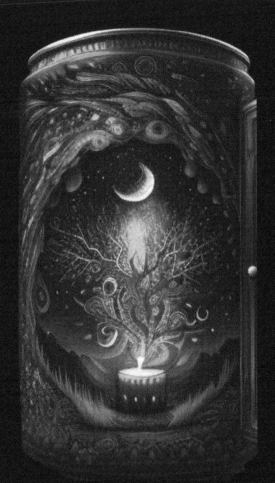

SPIRITWATERINC.COM

Made in the USA
Columbia, SC
09 September 2023

5cf79e14-61a5-4cc4-8e93-5c27020602f3R01